Games

Educators

Play

This effort is dedicated:

To my family: Rich, Amy, Lisa and Nathan
You fill my life with joy
          and
In memory of my parents:
John and Del Cirelli

Mary Jo Podgurski, RNC, MA, FACCE
Copyright, 1996 All rights reserved
Academy for Adolescent Health, Inc.
440 Washington Trust Building
Washington, Pa 15301
(724) 222-2311 Toll Free 1-(888) 222-2311

ISBN 1 - 891032 - 00 - 3

Games Educators Play Index

Introduction

I hear ..... and I forget

I see ...... and I remember

I do ...... and I Understand

....Chinese Proverb

Introduction

Think back to your earliest memory of a formal educational experience. Can you visualize yourself in school, seated at a small wooden desk identical to the small wooden desk of the child beside you? I can vividly recall being left in first grade by my tearful mother. Her apprehension didn't seem to impede my excitement; I remember being confused by her separation anxiety. By my way of thinking this was my first real adventure. To say that the six year old child I was then was hungry to learn is an understatement - I was breathless with anticipation. I remember my new dress and patent leather shoes, the smell of the new crayons I clutched in my fist and the coloring page that awaited me at that wooden desk as though these things were part of my recent past and didn't occur decades ago. My poor mother would tell the story of that day from her point of view: "I was so sad to leave her, and she just shook off my hand and went right inside the room. She never looked up to see if I was still there." I can't analyze the motives of my first grade self completely, but of one thing I'm crystal clear. I'd decided that learning would be fun. Wasn't it supposed to be?

In truth, it was my parents' fault that I expected to enjoy school. I was blessed with a wonderful mother and father, who were very wise, but had little formal schooling. My father immigrated to America as a fourteen year old and immediately began work in a glass factory, and my mother assumed responsibility for a large family of siblings when her own mother died young. In my preschool years, my parents literally delighted in my questions. I can picture them reading to me, and eventually, listening to me read to them. When we'd finish a book, they would close the book's cover and say: "Now we'll play the game. Let's see what you remember from what we just read." When I was tested in school, I was thrilled. I perceived testing as a chance to play my game of finding out how much I remembered!

Over the years of my education, through elementary and secondary schools, nursing school and undergraduate education, all the way through the completion of my master's thesis, I preserved that love of learning. But, over and over again, the system showed me how wrong I'd been about one of my assumptions. Learning most certainly wasn't always fun. I still think it should be.

Games have been part and parcel of our human existence since societies began to form. Every culture on the globe has their own versions of games. Place young children together and they create their own games, without boards or cards, without electronics or coaching. Perhaps that is the singular beauty of the human mind: the ability to create from one's own imagination.

The games in this book represent some of the workings of my imagination. Some of them grew out of hours of research and effort, while others arose spontaneously during a class session that I perceived to be dry. In 1989, when I began the Teen Outreach I now direct, I'd designate Games Days, when all the educational experiences were in the form of interactive games and role plays. It was no surprise to me when students responded enthusiastically to the curriculum on those days. Over time, games seemed to be encroaching more and more upon my class time. I lectured less and less, and enjoyed teaching more and more. I've grown with my students, and the education they've freely given to me is reflected here as well.

I've listed a "Birth Parent" for each of the games included in this manual to give credit to any professional who has contributed a game to this effort. To my knowledge, the games contained in these pages are original "Creations." Any resemblance to another person's creation is done without malice or pre-meditation. I mention that fact for one simple reason: it has been said that great minds think alike. If so, then educators who love to teach often think along the same lines. I was presenting a workshop across the country about two years ago and demonstrated a favorite game of mine. I'd never witnessed anyone play this game, nor had I ever read of it. Yet, an educator from the audience joined me for lunch and excitedly relayed her experience with the very same game idea - with slight variations that were so insignificant as to render the games nearly identical. We'd never met, had no prior contact by phone or e-mail, and had never attended the same seminars or conferences. I have no explanation for this phenomenon, except to pronounce the profound words of my youngest child: Go figure!

It is my hope that this manual will provide you with tools to reach out to your clients. In particular, I hope you will be inspired to expand your teaching to include more interactive techniques. I am convinced that interactive games and role play represent the gentlest, most respectful manner of teaching. While playing a game, we all release tension. We laugh, we have fun, we enjoy the gift of time we have together. In the midst of that pleasure, we also learn. It is my fervent belief that the learning that takes place in an informal fashion, without judgment, and with joy, is the purest and most powerful. Much research substantiates the fact that we retain most the things we do, not the things that we observe. By doing, my students are growing. I'm growing with them. I invite you to do the same.

I also would congratulate you on your choice of educational arenas. If you've chosen this manual, you have decided to work in health education. Working in the areas of childbirth, breastfeeding and parenting education is a great honor. I can conceive of no greater vocation than that of parenting, and assisting new families adjust is an important calling indeed. Tackling the rigors and controversy associated with sexuality education requires courage. I find myself growing spiritually with every day I teach in this area. I embrace you if you too are working hard on the front lines of this volatile topic. Our children's future is dependent upon your efforts. Way to go!

If you have comments about the games in this book, please feel free to contact me. I am also interested in any original games you'd be comfortable sharing for future editions of *Games Educators Play*. I can be reached at:

Mary Jo Podgurski
Academy for Adolescent Health, Inc.
440 Washington Trust Building
Washington, Pa 15301
Office Phone: (724) 222-2311; FAX: (724) 222-5406
Toll Free 1 (888) 301-2311
Website: www.healthyteens.com
e-mail: podmj@healthyteens.com

My wish for you in reading this manual is simple: I hope you enjoy what you find here.

Come, grow with me.

With friendship,

Mary Jo

**Academy for Adolescent Health, Inc.
Mission Statement**

MISSION STATEMENT

The mission of the Academy for Adolescent Health, Inc. is:

To serve youth, parents, professionals, and community by improving parent/youth communication, promoting healthy adolescent behavior, reducing risk, and encouraging wellness through quality parenting, childbirth, and sexuality education utilizing the Postpone, Prevent, Prepare[SM], POWER[SM], and E.C.H.O.[SM] curricula.

ONE KID AT A TIME!!

Chapter One
Why Games?

Learning....
should be a joy
and full of excitement

It is life's greatest
adventure

....Taylor Caldwell

Why Games?

Picture this: A classroom filled with orderly desks, in straight rows. Each desk holds a student, notebook in place, pen or pencil in hand. The teacher stands in front of the students, at a podium in the center of the room. Information is read by the teacher at the podium with little inflection as students struggle to take notes and remain awake. How much of the learning in that environment is retained? Research says precious little - perhaps 10%. How close does that picture approximate the vast majority of our educational experiences? Too close for comfort?

Now, take that same room and make a few changes. If you're the educator, isn't that your job, isn't this your domain, your stage? Circle the desks, or abandon them completely in favor of chairs in a circle or square. Divide students into small groups. Remember Anna and the King jockeying for power in the play *The King and I?* One person's position in relation to another conveys a subtle message. Don't tower above your students, but sit at their level.. Set groundrules and make promises that "set the stage" for informal learning. Establish trust. Model a relaxed affect. Smile. Explain your objectives, tell your student where you intend to go with this session, this class, this curriculum. Listen to their goals. Explore their ideas, respect their comments, encourage open discussion. And, most importantly, enjoy the great honor of teaching a class. Employ teaching as an art and embrace the title *educator* as a most treasured description of yourself. Your students will remember your classes, and return to you over and over again.

If you do permit your class to flow in this fashion, the most natural thing in the world will happen when you teach. You'll find yourself playing a game!

The fundamental reason for game playing in education lies with your clients. Whether they are adults or teens, young children or youth, everyone responds to fun. Retention of information is enhanced and tension is dissipated. Games allow for interaction, growth and student involvement. Vital life skills such as communication skills and group process are easily incorporated into game play. Student reaction to the games is crucial. Enthusiastic participation is positive reinforcement for educator and students alike.

Does this mean that we disregard other methods of teaching? Certainly not. Interspersing mini lectures, slide presentations, and group discussion within the framework of a class curriculum effectively reaches all types of learners. Be aware that lecture has been a foundation of our past educational experiences. Although lecture can be a one-sided effort with little opportunity for feedback from the student, it also represents a comfortable, familiar method of learning.

There are many ways to reach out to others, some of which "click" best with younger groups and some with adult learners. One of the concerns other professionals have voiced to me at workshops has been a fear of games or interactive techniques like role play simply not working. What does one do if no one volunteers, or if the technique you've tried falls flat? The answer to that comes from my heart: admit something's wrong, and ask the group to help analyze why. Some excellent discussion can arise in that situation. We need to remember that we're all learning, and none of us is perfect. An honest: "Something's not working with this? Anyone have any ideas where we're going wrong?" can open the door to areas of communication heretofore out of reach. Adolescents are particularly frank and will blurt out: "This is a stupid game, Mary Jo," if the situation warrants. I like to turn such a comment around and let the teen help modify the game, or even re-create it. Some of the best sessions we've had in the Teen Outreach have begun in just such a manner. An educator interested in really touching students must be flexible, able to fly without a lesson plan, and open to suggestion. With student involvement, your class will truly be a unique experience for student and educator alike.

Ways to Reach Out

Setting the Stage: Of primary importance is the climate or attitude of the session. This should be a unique educational experience, and the instructor should emulate relaxation with a positive, informal approach. (See Setting the Stage)

Icebreakers: Most experienced educators have a "toolbox" of icebreakers in reserve that are guaranteed to loosen up tense fathers and mothers to be. The use of icebreakers in a class with teens is a vital way to ease the tension they may be experiencing as a result of the strangeness of the topic (sex) or a new, untested instructor.

Games/Puzzles: Interactive games are the backbone of Postpone, Prevent, Prepare sm, and are received with enthusiasm by students. Of primary importance is *I Pass,* which enables the student the ability to avoid participation unless she/he is comfortable with the game.

Surveys/Discussion Sheets: Surveys may be done individually or in groups to stimulate discussion, and may be used to access prior knowledge or stimulate thought. Discussion sheets will spur conversation in small groups.

Humor: Humor is healing, and makes relaxation almost second nature. If an educator intends to work with adolescents, he/she needs humor both to lighten up a tense session and to survive under often stressful scenarios.

Story-Telling: Teaching in "parables" is a tried and true technique of master teachers throughout history. Participants respond to the familiar tone and attitude of stories.

Role Plays: My personal favorite. I avoid scripted role plays since they stifle creativity and often result of mocking attitudes from teens who focus upon a part of the script that seems alien or stilted instead of the message. Once more, *I Pass* is firmly in place. If possible, the instructor should initiate the role play by being a participant to break the ice. (See Role Play)

Review: The utilization of games, puzzles and surveys may camouflage the fact that the same material is being covered and make it more fun.

Laugh. Enjoy your Students. Ultimately, HAVE FUN. It's Contagious!!!

Professional Survey

The survey on the following pages is meant for your own use. I find that a little "self" examination before considering interactive learning experiences can be very helpful. The information is for your own insight. I tell the students in our Teen Outreach to please, please, STOP and THINK. Those are wise words for professionals as well. Our personal prejudices color the way we approach a class. If we've had a negative experience with role play or game playing, the chances are we won't be comfortable introducing the concept to our clients. Enjoy yourself as you open the door to "playing" in class!

You may choose to utilize this survey in a professional workshop or Inservice. If so, I give permission for the survey's duplication, (the survey only), provided you don't edit it in anyway or remove the copyright. I find that some well-intentioned educators tend to copy "at will" on occasion, and hope that you will be respectful of my wishes. You may add the statement:

"Permission given to duplicate this survey for _____ workshop" to the survey.

I will also need to be informed in writing that you intend to duplicate the survey. I would greatly appreciate any feedback you receive from conducting the survey.

Please consider the labor of your own original work, and copyright anything you have become a "Birth Parent" to yourself. Don't be afraid of your own creativity. Value yourself highly. Your efforts are laudable and worthy of respect.

As always, thank you for your interest in reaching out to others.

"Games Educators Play" Survey

Mary Jo Podgurski, RNC, MA, FACCE
Academy for Adolescent Health, Inc.
440 Washington Trust Building
Washington, Pa 15301
(412) 222-2311 Toll Free 1 (888) 301-2311

The following information is offered to help clarify your own learning style, as well as assist you in understanding the learning style in which you prefer to teach. REMEMBER that there is no one perfect teaching method. Master teachers think of their students first. The cultural diversity of their students is an intricate challenge. Understanding student motives helps design your curriculum; knowing your students, their personalities, and learning styles, helps design the instruction.

The true order of learning should be:
First, what is necessary; second what is useful, and third, what is ornamental.
To reverse this arrangement is like beginning to build at the top of the edifice.

Lydia H. Sigourney

The following questions ask about your educational experience as a child and young adult:

1. Did you enjoy going to school as a child? (Grades 1 - 5 in particular)
_____ Yes
_____ No

2. Which grade in elementary school is the first you remember clearly: _____

3. Can you picture your favorite teacher in elementary school? _____
What about this teacher made him or her your favorite?
_____

4. What class (subject) did you most enjoy in your elementary school experience?
_____

5. Did you attend a "middle school" (grades 6 - 8 or 6 - 9)
_____ Yes
_____ No

6. What stands out in your memory about those years in school?
_____

7. List the following in their order of importance to you when you were in grade 6 - 9:
_____ Family
_____ Friends
_____ Media (TV, radio, movies)
_____ Teachers _____

Education is the transmission of civilization

Ariel and Will Durant

8. Do you remember any teacher in grades 1 - 8 who used role play or interactive games in your class?

_____ Yes

_____ No

9. If you answered yes in question 8, what do you remember about that experience?

_____

10. Describe your favorite high school (grades 9 or 1 - 12) teacher:

_____

What set him or her apart in your mind?

_____

11. What type of education did you attend after high school? (please list all degrees or diplomas)

_____

_____

_____

_____

12. During these experiences as an adult learner, do you remember feeling:

_____ More at ease than while a child or adolescent in school

_____ Under more pressure than while a child or adolescent in school

_____ A sense of excitement regarding the learning experience

_____ A feeling of needing to "jump through hoops" to achieve goals that were often   boring

_____ A genuine sense of growth and accomplishment

_____ Frustration at the quality of professors available to you

13. During your post-high school experiences, did you regularly participate in:

_____ Role play

_____ Interactive learning games

_____ The use of audiovisual 35 mm slides

_____ The use of movies or videos

14. Did you dread being called upon to participate in exercises or role plays?

_____ Yes

_____ No

15. Did you commonly play any of the following as a child or adolescent:

_____ Board games

_____ Organized sports

_____ Card games

We teach what we learn, and the cycle goes on

Joan Curcio

The following questions apply to your experience as an educator and adult:

16. Do you regularly volunteer to participate in the following:
_____ Leading a church service
_____ Leading a song
_____ Organizing a practical joke on a friend
_____ Heading a committee
_____ Serving on a parent- teacher organization as an officer
_____ Serving as a board member in an organization

17. Have you ever run for office (in any capacity)?
_____ Yes
_____ No

18. Are you a parent?
_____ Yes
_____ No

19. If yes, do you regularly "Play" with your children?
_____ Yes
_____ No

20. When you describe yourself, do you include "teacher" or "educator" as part of your description?
_____ Yes
_____ No

21. How long have you thought of yourself as a "teacher"? _____

22. What was your first real teaching experience?
_____

22. Have you been formally trained as a teacher (graduating with a degree in education)?
_____ Yes
_____ No

23. When you teach, do you regularly use:
_____ Role play
_____ Interactive games
_____ Audiovisual 35 mm slides
_____ Videos or movies

24. Have you ever "created" a game for use in a class?
_____ Yes
_____ No

(My mother) said that I must always be intolerant of ignorance but understanding of illiteracy.
That some people, unable to go to school, were more educated
and more intelligent than college professors

Maya Angelou

25. If you have created a game for class use, please describe it:

_____
_____
_____

26. IF you utilize games or role play in your teaching, do you participate in them yourself?
_____ Yes
_____ No

27. When you attend a workshop or seminar, what is your primary goal? (please list one)

_____ Getting your money's worth
_____ Obtaining knowledge for knowledge's sake
_____ Obtaining continuing education units
_____ Advancing your career
_____ Providing a diversion in your everyday work week
_____ Being entertained

28. What do you most like to do at a workshop or seminar?
_____ Be lectured to
_____ Taking notes
_____ Being given handouts
_____ An outline
_____ Small group work
_____ Participating in games or role plays

29. What do you least like at a workshop or seminar:
_____ To be lectured to
_____ Taking notes
_____ Being given handouts
_____ An outline
_____ Small group work
_____ Participating in games or role plays

30. Did you mind filling out this survey?
_____ Yes
_____ No

Comments

_____
_____
_____

Chapter Two
Setting the Stage

Good teaching
is
one-fourth preparation
and
three-fourth theater

....Gail Godwin

Setting the Stage

Nothing is more vital to a successful interactive experience than "setting the stage." Participants need to know where the group is going as well as what philosophy the educator embraces. Imagine yourself on a cruise ship. Not only would you want to know your destination, you would be interested in the motives of the captain at the helm! People who participate in an interactive game or role play need to have trust in the educator or group leader. It is crucial, then, that the "stage" for each class be set by establishing groundrules and attitudes that provide comfort and ease tension.

Story-telling: Begin with a short story that relays your motives, your passion, and your reason for being with the group. It is important that your students understand where you're coming from before they entrust you to take them anywhere educationally.

Humor: Set the tone as an informal one with humor that laughs *with* others, not *at* them.

Tone: Model an open, non-judgmental affect that is both approachable and relaxed.

Groundrules: All Outreach sessions have groundrules. Some are tried and true and exist in every session, while others are determined group by group. Some of the most important are:

- **"I Pass" - No one is ever forced to participate. No game, no role play, no discussion, is ever assigned. This is the most important rule for a relaxed, enjoyable session or class.**

- **Anyone may speak freely, but one person speaks at a time.**

- **Questions will be answered.**

- **Respect and Dignity - All persons, regardless of race, gender, belief system, sexual orientation, or social status in the group, will be treated with respect and dignity. No demeaning humor, no "put downs" and no judgment calls from the educator will be allowed.**

- **Non-Judgmental - Strive to be as non-judgmental as possible.**

- **Honesty - Promise to be truthful. If a question is asked that the educator doesn't have an answer for, one will be researched and brought back to class.**

- **Confidentiality - the ability to speak openly with the educator without fear of repercussion - should be introduced. Limits of confidentiality need to be explained. For example, when working with** youth it is vital that an educator be aware of potential legal issues, including the difficult and painful situations surrounding rape, child abuse or neglect. Most states have laws that mandate reporting child abuse.

Teens should be told up front that their confidences will stay with the educator unless danger is involved. In that event, the teen should know someone else (for example, guidance personnel in the school, children and youth services, or police) will have to be informed. Whenever possible, young people should have say in how others will be informed. In other words, although the proper reporting will take place, it won't do so behind the teen's back.

Game Rules: Explain the play of the game clearly and slowly. Take care to repeat the instructions more than once. Be especially sensitive to the perception of your students. In other words, model respect if a student misses a cue in role play or is confused about how a game is played.

Make Every Session Count: Approach every class as if it were a major presentation at a national conference. Treat your "everyday" students as if their feedback to you is just as important as that of your employer. In other words, pretend this group of students is paying you a sizable honorarium (you wish) and are expecting great things of this session. As educators, we may not know when we made a difference in a student's life. Approach each student as if you will make a difference, and you may.

Be Flexible: Adapt games to the group at hand.

Have a Formal Beginning and Closing to your Program: I learned this technique from my days as a Girl Scout Leader. As informal as my programs are, I know how much people enjoy ceremony. Our Outreach employees meet for staffing weekly. We begin with a formal reading or prayer, and then embark into informal discussion, one staff member at a time. Beginning with some type of event that "sets off" the class - music, a reading, a quote - sets the tone. A student could be asked to provide such an activity. Only a few moments will be needed for such for an entry and closing ceremony, but the experience will usually "stick" with your students.

Do a Wrap Up or Re-Cap: On-going evaluation is not only healthy, it can be life-sustaining. Let your students know how much you appreciate their feedback at the onset of the session and don't forget to ask for it formally, in writing, at the end.

Finally, Sustain Yourself: You've chosen a difficult avenue of education. Seeking to affect behavioral change is tough, but rewarding. Sustain yourself with continuing education, workshops and professional contacts. Belong to your professional organization and become an active member. You'll receive much more than you give. Find your spiritual base and re-new yourself spiritually before and after sessions. A few moments of quiet relaxation, meditation or prayer before you "go on stage" can provide lingering support in difficult situations.

Let me know how your games "click" .....I'd love to hear from you.

Remember - "Set the Stage" First

♦ **Prepare Your Self**

♦ **Prepare Your Students**

       Story-telling
       Humor
       Tone

♦ **Groundrules**

       "I Pass"
       Open Environment
       Questions and Answers
       Respect and Dignity
       Non-judgmental Attitude
       "Boring?"
       "Too Gross?"
       Confidentiality

♦ **Game Rules**

♦ **Be Flexible**

♦ **Student Led Projects**

♦ **Review, Review, Review**

♦ **Closing**

Chapter Three
Games for
Childbirth
Education

*In the sheltered simplicity of the
first days after a baby is born,
one sees again the magical closed
circle, the miraculous sense of
two people existing only for each other*

.... Anne Morrow Lindbergh

Name that Tune

Subject: Music for tension release
Target Population: Expectant parents
Suitable For: Any age group, mixed gender
Props Needed: Tape or CD player,
  Assorted music
  Paper and pencil

Time: Approximately 15 minutes

OVERVIEW
Name that Tune is simple and fun to play. Individual taste in music may be expanded as participants are exposed to varying types of relaxation tunes.

BEHAVIORAL OBJECTIVES
At the end of the game, the participants will be able to:
♦ State the theory behind release of tension as a non-pharmocologic method of pain relief
♦ List two reasons for utilizing music to release tension
♦ Name three types of music they find appealing

PREPARATION - "Setting the Stage"
This is one of the simplest games I play, and one of the most fun! I introduce the game the week before I intend to play, and invite the class to bring their favorite music with them next week. This is especially appealing to adolescents (who will undoubtedly turn up with music you may not have associated with relaxation!) Don't be afraid to experiment. If your class trusts you, they'll tell you which sounds help them ease tension and which don't! Choose a set number of pieces prior to play, so that the class is able to number their papers accordingly. An example of relaxation music is included in the bibliography.

 HOW TO PLAY
Play of the Game
Each participant numbers his/her paper from 1 - 10 (or the number of musical selections you've chosen) and then writes down what he/she thinks each piece of music means to them as the educator plays it. At the end of the playing time, those who wish may volunteer to say what they think the piece represents out loud. Each member of class will then choose their Favorite Musical Selection. Then, the expectant mom and her partner switch the numbered sheets of paper to discover how each of them rated the sounds. Finally, the entire class votes on the coveted Best Tension Releaser Sound (Move over, Grammies!!) This is fun, easy, and involves discussion that can really lead to communication for the mom and her partner

Educator Tips
Vary the type of music used, being certain to preview unfamiliar pieces prior to the class.
Introduce "new" sounds, attempting to get past your own personal preference and be open to your clients' needs.

Labor and Birth Flashcards

Subject: Labor knowledge and skills review
Target Population: Expectant parents
Suitable For: Any age group, mixed gender
Props Needed: Cards (as below)

Time: Approximately 20 - 30 minutes

OVERVIEW
Labor and Birth Flashcards provide a review of materiel covered in prior classes. The use of the flatcars can also encourage communication between partners

BEHAVIORAL OBJECTIVES
At the end of the game, the participants will be able to:
♦   Review three topics pertinent to prepared childbirth
♦   Communicate two areas of concern regarding labor and birth to their partner

---

PREPARATION - "Setting the Stage"
Prepare cards in advance with questions appropriate for review. I prefer two primary topics: Labor/birth skills and Labor/birth knowledge. I've accumulated questions from couples over the years and find that the same kinds of things need to be reviewed. Examples: contractions timing; when to go to the hospital; which skill is most useful with an urge to push, during tough contractions, etc. ; labor positions; "panic" routine; assertive responses.

 HOW TO PLAY
Play of the Game
I enjoy playing this game at the final class, while I'm spending private time with each woman and her partner. We take a long break - approximately a half hour. During this time, the Flash Cards are passed out for each couple to work on independently. I play a postpartum or child care video at one end of the room for folks who choose to pass on the review (although few do). There should always be some background music or sound in the classroom to provide privacy as the couples work through their questions. This is also an excellent time for couples to do evaluations of the class, and register for reunions. Explain the game and distribute cards to each dyad. After the break, review all the answers aloud to the entire group

 Educator Tips
Avoid embarrassing anyone. It is vital that all class members feel a sense of safety. Never "put someone on the spot" or belittle them!

Myth or Fact

Subject: Common myths about pregnancy, labor and birth
Target Population: Expectant parents
Suitable For: Any age group, mixed gender
Props Needed: Cards
Sense of humor

Time: Approximately 10 minutes

OVERVIEW
The Myth or Fact **Game** has a double focus. It contributes to the easing of tension in a childbirth class (laughter invariably follows some of the cards!). Correcting common misbeliefs without embarrassing a participant who has been told an Old Wives Tale and may hesitate to inquire of its credibility is an added benefit.

BEHAVIORAL OBJECTIVES
At the end of the game, the participants will be able to:
♦ Describe the difference between an "Old Wives Tale" and fact
♦ List three myths about pregnancy, labor or birth that can be demeaning or detrimental to an expectant mother

PREPARATION
Prepare cards detailing common myths of pregnancy and labor. For example, the many and myriad myths regarding the gender of the baby can be used as an icebreaker in this fast moving game. Common misconceptions regarding the safety of mother and babe (for example, if the mother raised her hands above her head, the cord wraps around the baby's neck) can be interspersed with more factual information. Be careful that not all the cards are false...some should manifest true situations.

 HOW TO PLAY
Play of the Game
Distribute the cards during the second or third class session. Each class member reads the contents of the card in turn, and the educator reacts to it. Any one should be permitted to respond, however, and the reader should never be made to feel as if he/she must "have the right answer"

 Educator Tips
Keep your ears open! It's amazing how my card selection has grown over the years as I'm told more and more old wives tales! Remember the "I Pass" rule.

What Would YOU Do?

Subject: Possible pregnancy, labor or birth scenarios
Target Population: Expectant parents
Suitable For: All age groups
Props Needed: Cards (as below)

Time: Approximately 15 minutes

OVERVIEW
The What Would You Do? Game can be a very enlightening game for in class play. Its focus is as an introductory role play that allows for open communication between partners.

BEHAVIORAL OBJECTIVES
At the end of the game, the participants will be able to:
♦ Discuss possible reactions to common pregnancy and birth scenarios

---

PREPARATION - "Setting the Stage"
Prepare cards explaining possible scenarios that involve pregnancy, labor and birth. While not actually a role play, this game is a good preparation for it, and can be useful in introducing role play concepts without even mentioning the words! (Sneaky, right?) Cards should be in two colors, and should be marked either: For Expectant Mother or For Support Person   Some of my favorites:

For Expectant Mother: You are at the beauty parlor and begin to have very hard, strong contractions, coming frequently. Only one side of your hair is cut. What would you do?

For Support Person: Your partner is having mild, somewhat regular contractions. She demands a hot fudge sundae. Do you race out the door to get her one? If so, will you have one too?

 **HOW TO PLAY**

Play of the Game
Distribute cards, making certain that each person receives one marked for their own role in this experience - either mother or support person. (A fun variation of this game involves switching roles - the next step to introducing role play to reluctant participants)

 Educator Tips
Once more, bear in mind that no one likes to be put on the spot. I find it easier to let my class lead the way. If the group is cohesive and has been open, with easy, free-flowing discussion, they may be ready to do this in a group, with each member being handed a card. If not, the game is better played in small groups or dyads.
There are no wrong answers. Model accepting behavior, and laugh a lot!

Answer that Phone! (Post-partum)

Subject: Reality based post-partum game
Target Population: Expectant parents
Suitable For: All age groups
Props Needed: Two phones
Various child care books
Cards with scenarios (as below)

Time: Approximately 20 minutes

OVERVIEW
Answer that Phone is a non threatening role play that focuses upon coping and parenting skills postpartum. This game models good phone etiquette, helps the parents formalize their thoughts prior to calling their careprovider, and attempts to remove the stereotype of "bothering the doctor"

BEHAVIORAL OBJECTIVES
At the end of the game, the participants will be able to:
♦   Demonstrate responses to common postpartum scenarios

PREPARATION - "Setting the Stage"
Prepare several possible scenarios - for example, "Is your baby ill? Her skin feels hot to your touch, she's fussy, and won't nurse. Call the pediatrician and explain the problem."

 **HOW TO PLAY**
Play of the Game
One phone goes to a member of the class who volunteers to be the new parent. The other class members utilize the books and help him or her to make their decision...do they call, what do they say, how hard do they press for the baby to be seen.

A member of the class can "play" the pediatrician, or care provider, but I find it less threatening the first time if the educator assumes that role. I also like to throw in a disgruntled overworked office staff who initially answers the phone and dismisses the new parent's concerns. It's quite interesting to play this one when you actually do have a physician or pediatric nurse in the class!!

 **Educator Tips**
Be creative with this one. Bear in mind that your attitude could model disdain for a careprovider if you're not careful. Although you want the parent to be assertive if need be, you also want to convey the caring attitude of the careprovider and his/her staff

Answer that Phone! (Labor)

Subject: Reality Based Labor Game
Target Population: Expectant parents
Suitable For: All age groups
Props Needed: Two phones
Cards (as below)

Time: Approximately 10 minutes

OVERVIEW
Answer that Phone (Labor) is role play that focuses upon needs of a women who is unsure about her status in labor.

BEHAVIORAL OBJECTIVES
At the end of the game, the participants will be able to:
♦ Name two signs of labor
♦ Demonstrate proper technique for calling caregiver
♦ List three items of information to give to caregiver during the phone call

PREPARATION
Prepare scenarios that will enable the expectant mother and her partner to "walk through" a phone call to her careprovider, asking, for example, if she should be seen in the office (she's experiencing blood show) or should go to the hospital (she has some symptoms of labor, but is unsure)

 HOW TO PLAY
Play of the Game
One phone goes to a member of the class. The other class members help him or her to make their decision...do they call, what do they say, how hard do they press to NOT go to the hospital too soon.

Educator Tips
Be creative. Once more, bear in mind that your attitude could model disdain for a careprovider if you're not careful. This is also an excellent chance to review signs of labor and physical and emotional needs for support.

An Academy Award Presentation

Subject: "Real" Women in "Real" Labor
Target Population: Expectant parents
Suitable For: All age groups, but teens really love it!
Props Needed: Your right brain!!

Time: Dependent upon the "Actor" in you - approximately 10 minutes

OVERVIEW
An Academy Award Presentation is a good first role play because the educator provides the acting. This game models realistic labor and labor skills while encouraging discussion on labor support.

BEHAVIORAL OBJECTIVES
At the end of the game, the participants will be able to:
♦ List responses a support person may make if a woman "panics" in labor

---

PREPARATION - "Setting the Stage"
Practice, practice, practice. In front of a mirror, in front of your poor family, in front of colleagues. When your first "performance" arrives, you'll still be not quite ready, which is great! That means you'll improvise!!

 HOW TO PLAY
Play of the Game
Introduce the concept: You (the educator) is a laboring woman who is having mild contractions with her first labor. She is coping extremely well, and is using slow paced breathing with relaxation and an internal focus of imagery. She looks like a Lamaze movie!! Then, suddenly, nature intervenes, and - right in the middle of a "mild" contraction - you guessed it, the "real labor" you're going to act out. Instruct the class - both moms and partners - that they are YOUR partner in this next exercise. Ask them to watch your behavior and tell you what they would do to help support you.

 Educator Tips
Introduce this after a successful relaxing and breathing practice, preferably before a break, but not before you dismiss the class! This will "wake up" people, and a wind down discussion is vital. REMEMBER, your reactions should be reality based. Don't model your own response to strong contractions, but rather manifest a composite of many women you've observed. BE CAREFUL to show something that is doable, and is survivable. No screaming, no really out of control stuff for theatrics sake. Just loose your focus, speed up your breathing, clutch the sheet or pillow, shift position, rub your back vigorously, let your facial expression show distress.

© 1996 *Games Educators Play*
"Birth Parent" for this game = Mary Jo Podgurski, RNC, MA, FACCE

Chapter Four
Games for
Puberty
Education

The Teacher's Task
is to Initiate the Process
and then
GET
OUT
of the WAY

....John **Wharton**

Visualize It - Me, a Parent? #1!

Subject: Identifying with parenting as an adult activity
Target Population: Works best with late elementary and middle school students, although may be successfully used at the secondary school level as well
Suitable For: Males, females or co-ed groups
Props Needed: None
                            Time: Approximately 5 minutes, 15 minutes with optional discussions

OVERVIEW

Visualize It - Me, a Parent? #1 is a quick, simple game with serious overtones. It can be used to introduce the concept of parenting as a choice, and ideally should follow some work on decision making and refusal skills. Although deceptively easy, it can serve as a springboard for several excellent discussion topics.

BEHAVIORAL OBJECTIVES

At the end of the game, the participants will be able to:
♦   Define parenting as an adult activity
♦   Discuss reasons for avoiding early childbearing

PREPARATION - "Setting the Stage"
The only preparation needed for this quick but efficient game is the development of an early trust relationship between students and educator. Asking students to close their eyes to participate could engender apprehension and should only be initiated once some rapport is established. **Give participants the right to "Pass."**

 **HOW TO PLAY**

Play of the Game
The educator asks the students to close their eyes briefly while the game is played. The educator will announce several ages, beginning with the ages of the students involved. The students are instructed to raise their hands when the age at which they'd like to be a mother or father has been reached. The educator should continue the "ages" until menopausal ages for a female group, and later ages for a male group. Discretion of the educator should be utilized for co-ed groups. Post game discussion can evolve from reasons to delay childbearing until adulthood to the choice of ages used - for e.g., why do women stop bearing children at certain ages, while men may become fathers must longer.

 Educator Tips

Students close their eyes to allow for individualization. With eyes open they often get caught up in what their peers are doing! State that some students may not raise their hands, signifying their feeling at this time that they may not be parents. Optional discussion can then lead into parenting as a career, as a choice, as a live calling. Once more, this game is best played after the introduction of decision making and refusal skills.

Visualize It - Me, a Parent? #2 !

Subject: Considering the consequences of early childbearing
Target Population: Works best with late elementary and middle school students, although may be successfully used at the secondary school level as well
Suitable For: Males, females or co-ed groups
Props Needed: None
                                        Time: Approximately 5 minutes, 15 minutes with optional discussion

OVERVIEW

Visualize It - Me, a Parent? #2 is a continuation of *Visualize It - Me, a Parent? #1.*   It can be used to reinforce and enlarge upon the concept of parenting as an adult activity, stressing the long term consequences of early childbearing.   It also is deceptively easy, and can serve as a springboard for several excellent discussion topics.

BEHAVIORAL OBJECTIVES

At the end of the game, the participants will be able to:

♦   Acknowledge parenting as an adult activity
♦   Discuss long term consequences of early childbearing

PREPARATION - "Setting the Stage"

This game should follow *Visualize It - Me, a Parent? #1.*   Students are typically very comfortable expanding this concept.   It is usually helpful for this aspect of the game to give a brief introduction to the concept of visualization prior to beginning.   I find the idea easy to explain if I use the analogy of "daydreaming" - something all kids are able to do.   Asking the students to take a few slow breaths and release tension helps as well.   **Give participants the right to "Pass."**

 **HOW TO PLAY**

Play of the Game

The educator asks the students to close their eyes briefly while the game is played.   The educator will then ask students to imagine themselves as they will be ten years from now.   The educator should then ask some simple questions: How old will you be ten years from now? Where do you think you will live then? At your current home, or on your own? Are you in college, working, or in the military? Do you have a car? If so, what kind of car? Questions should enable students to create an image of themselves in the future.   Once that picture is made, the educator should ask: Do you have a baby? A child of five or six? If you are a parent, how do you think your baby or child would change the picture you've painted? Could you live away from your parents if you were a parent yourself? Where would your money come from? Etc.

 Educator Tips

Avoid "taking" a student somewhere with visual imagery as a suggestion.   Remind the students that they are to answer the questions "in their heads."   Avoid preaching or lecturing by letting the students lead post game discussions.

What's Going On?

Subject: Physical and emotional changes associated with puberty
Target Population: Late elementary and middle school students
Suitable For: Males, females, parent attended classes
Props Needed: None

Time: Approximately 30 minutes

OVERVIEW

What's Going On? is a fun way to introduce the changes associated with puberty. Students seem to enjoy this informal format, and discussion can easily flow from students to educator during the play of the game.

BEHAVIORAL OBJECTIVES

At the end of the game, the participants will be able to:

♦   List three physical changes associated with puberty
♦   List three emotional changes associated with puberty
♦   Discuss concept of Normalcy - "OK" for each individual growing up

---

PREPARATION - "Setting the Stage"
Prepare cards with the following words printed in large, easily read letters: Moods, Feet, Under arm Hair, Facial Hair, Chest Hair, Pubic Hair, Skin, Shoulders, Chest, Breasts, Voice Penis, Scrotum, Ovum, Sperm, Periods, Wet Dreams, Ovulation, Ejaculation. I find it useful to color code cards with male and female changes, with a third color for changes that occur in both genders. **Give participants the right to "Pass."**

 HOW TO PLAY

Play of the Game
Cards are distributed one at a time to student volunteers to take them. The student may either read the word on the card or simply hold it up for all to see. Group discussion will center on what the word refers to in conjunction with puberty - for example, feet reach adult size earlier than the rest of the body, so that incredible foot growth experienced in middle school will eventually halt! Some of the words have more potential for embarrassment than others. I recommend introducing Moods and Feet first, and then moving in order of the topic's typical occurrence during puberty, alternating gender changes.

 Educator Tips

Providing a basic foundation in puberty can be a very dry and boring subject. At the same time, many students are intensely interested in the topic, but hesitant about broaching it. This game should be an informal way to discuss a potentially tough subject. Be aware of the developmental levels of your student group, and observe each child for signs of discomfort. Ideally this game is taught in a group of 8 - 15.

Color Me!

Subject: Anatomy
Target Population: Late elementary and middle school students
Suitable For: Males, females, parent attended classes
Props Needed: Coloring books or handouts of human anatomy
                Crayons

                                        Time: Approximately 30 minutes

OVERVIEW
Color Me is an innovative way to introduce reproductive anatomy.

BEHAVIORAL OBJECTIVES
At the end of the game, the participants will be able to:
♦ Name three correct terms for parts of the male genitalia
♦ Name three correct terms for parts of the male genitalia
♦ Discuss the connection between male genitalia and spermatogenesis
♦ Discuss the connection between female genitalia and ovulation

---

PREPARATION - "Setting the Stage"
Prepare a coloring book or handout of both male and female reproductive organs. Ideally the anatomy should be large enough for the student to color, yet be superimposed within a full body. "Floating" body parts, for example, a uterus pictured separate from the female form, may be confusing to young people with no prior frame of reference. The educator should partially color a copy of the handout prior to the session, and continue coloring each part with the students.

 HOW TO PLAY
Play of the Game
Students are asked to color the pictures of male and female reproductive organs. They may color the picture in any way they like. Discussion and questions should flow freely as the students color.

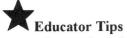Educator Tips
In our Outreach, only the most fundamental anatomical information is addressed. It is my belief that "Nuts and Bolts" or anatomy too often passes for sexuality education in our schools. Alone, this information will do little to postpone sexual involvement or effect behavioral change. In other words, correct knowledge of the number of Fallopian tubes will do little to decrease teen pregnancy rates without refusal and decision making skills as well. This exercise simply seeks to give basic information to enhance discussion.

Care should be taken to model respect for diversity in this exercise as in all class activities. Pictures of young people should represent the face of America: African-American, Euro-American, Hispanic American, and Asian American faces should be part of the coloring pages.

What Will I Look Like - Draw Me!

Subject: Physical changes of puberty
Target Population: Late elementary and middle school students
Suitable For: Males, females, parent attended classes
Props Needed: Blank paper
                Crayons

Time: Approximately 10 minutes

OVERVIEW

What Will I Look Like - Draw Me is a creative way to encourage self-expression as puberty approaches. Students who participate will have an opportunity to imagine their future selves in a positive way.

BEHAVIORAL OBJECTIVES

At the end of the game, the participants will be able to:

♦ Define puberty
♦ Discuss possible changes in their bodies during the years of puberty
♦ Set future goals

PREPARATION - "Setting the Stage"
Prepare several examples of young people's self-portraits of puberty.

 HOW TO PLAY

Play of the Game
Students are asked to draw a simple picture of themselves as they imagine they will look at the end of puberty. A second picture may be of their perception of themselves now, and a third of the way they think they'll look in the years of puberty, as their bodies change. Discussion should flow during the drawing, and may center upon emotions engendered by the physical changes they'll experience.

Educator Tips

This game usually "clicks" or works. If it doesn't and your students seem reluctant to participate in the drawing, I suggest the *What will I Look Like Ad Game* on the next page.

What Will I Look Like - Ad Game

Subject: Physical changes of puberty
Target Population: Late elementary and middle school students
Suitable For: Males, females, parent attended classes
Props Needed: Magazine
      Scissors
      Cut out advertisements showing children, youth, and adult body types
      Chalkboard, flip chart, or marking board
             Time: Approximately 15 minutes

OVERVIEW
What Will I Look Like - Ad Game is a enhance understanding of puberty change as well as analyze advertisements.

BEHAVIORAL OBJECTIVES
At the end of the game, the participants will be able to:
♦ Discuss possible changes in their bodies during the years of puberty
♦ List three ways advertisements pre-condition young people to a certain kind of adult body type

---

PREPARATION - "Setting the Stage"
Pictures depicting human beings at various ages should be cut out from popular magazines and laminated. These pictures should represent as many races as possible. Magazines should have several ads of people at different stages of growth and development.

 HOW TO PLAY
Play of the Game
Students are asked to identify what stage of human growth and development the models in magazine pictures represents. Activity surrounding the cutting out of new pictures should stimulate discussion of: male and female role models, suggestive attitudes of the models, body type, accuracy of pictures as associated with normal people in student's lives, etc.

Educator Tips
This game is a good opportunity to introduce gender roles, concern over eating disorders such as anorexia and bulimia, and drug and alcohol abuse in professional models.

Candy Game

Subject: Decision making skills
Target Population: Students of all ages
Suitable For: Males, females, co-ed groups
Props Needed: Various kinds of individually wrapped candy as recommended
　　　　　　Large plastic jar
　　　　　　Chalkboard, flip chart, or marking board

Time: Approximately 10 minutes

OVERVIEW

The Candy Game is well liked by all ages and serves as an excellent activity for warm up and reinforcement of decision making skills

BEHAVIORAL OBJECTIVES

At the end of the game, the participants will be able to:

♦　List five steps to making a decision
♦　Evaluate a non-threatening decision

PREPARATION - "Setting the Stage"
Candy should be purchased in the following types and mixed in the plastic jar:
Red Fire Balls (Or another type of hot or spicy candy)
Yellow Lemon Heads (Or another type of sour candy)
Mixed Jolly Ranchers (Or another type of sweet candy)
Multi-colored Neon Bandits or Tongue Splashers (Or another type of candy that colors the mouth)
A handout on decision making should be developed detailing the steps of making an informed decision. The flip chart or chalkboard may be used if handouts aren't available

---

 HOW TO PLAY

Play of the Game
Students are told they will have a chance to choose a candy from the jar. Steps to healthy decision making are reviewed before the selection. When all the students have chosen a piece of candy, an analogy of sexuality is introduced: Do any of the students feel that they got more than they expected, in a negative way? (The candy is hotter or more sour than anticipated) If they choose a candy that leaves the mouth colored, can they hide the fact that they made that choice? Discussion can easily move into gender stereotypes and different labeling that occurs if male or female students engage in sexual activity. Even now, in the nineties, social consensus in Outreach schools continues to judge the female in a negative way and the male in a positive way.

 Educator Tips

A variation of the game is to ask the students to close their eyes and take a candy without going through the decision making process. A student commented after this variation: "Sex is like Mary Jo's candy jar. You never know what you're gonna get!"

Grab Bag Game

Subject: Menstruation
Target Population: Students of all ages
Suitable For: Males, females, co-ed groups, parent attended classes
Props Needed: Lunch bags
         Sanitary napkins - various types and styles
         Tampons - various types and styles
         Small statue of three month old fetus
         Pocket uterus and baby
         Old sanitary napkin belt
         Pocket calendar
         Quarters
         Herbal tea bag
         Something that suggests exercise - head band, small weights, etc
         Cards .

Time: Approximately 15 minutes

OVERVIEW
The Grab Bag Game is can be used in numerous variations. In this game, objects associated with menstruation are touched and discussed in an informal, relaxed fashion.

BEHAVIORAL OBJECTIVES
At the end of the game, the participants will be able to:
- Identify objects needed during menstruation
- Discuss proper hygiene for young women
- List choices that will enhance good health

PREPARATION - "Setting the Stage"
Items for play should be placed in the bags and the bags should then be taped shut. The cards should each contain a slang term for menstruation: "Falling off the roof, the curse, come sick, a visit from my Aunt Rosy, etc."

 HOW TO PLAY
Play of the Game
Each student individually chooses a bag and opens it as the others in the group sit in a circle and look on. Discussion revolves around each selection: How does it connect with menstruation? How is the product used? What do the students think of this product, or item? How did the slang terms evolve? What implications do they have for women's self image?

 Educator Tips
Remember to respect the "I Pass" rule. The student may only feel comfortable opening the bag, in which case the other students or the educator should initiate discussion on its contents. Water may be provided for the students to "play" with tampons while another activity is offered for parents.

Guess a Number

Subject: Spermatogenesis
Target Population: Students of all ages
Suitable For: Males, females, co-ed groups, parent attended classes
Props Needed: Large binder filled with pages of small commas to total one million
      Chalkboard, flip chart, or wipe off board

Time: Approximately 5 minutes

OVERVIEW
The Guess a Number Game is a fast, simple, and participatory game. It makes a concept that is difficult to conceptualize tangible in a quick way.

BEHAVIORAL OBJECTIVES
At the end of the game, the participants will be able to:
♦ Identify correct numbers of sperm produced by healthy young men
♦ Name the number of sperm necessary for conception

PREPARATION - "Setting the Stage"
A single page filled with small commas should be typed and counted. Pages should be duplicated until the total of commas in the binder reach one million. The students call this binder my "sperm book"

 HOW TO PLAY

Play of the Game
The binder is passed around to all students, who are given an opportunity to turn the pages and examine it. The idea of each comma representing one sperm is introduced. Students are then asked to guess how many binders, or "sperm books," would be needed to demonstrate the number of sperm a healthy young man makes daily. Guesses are written on the board, and students vote for the number they think is closest to the truth. 100- 200 million (100 - 200 books) is seldom chosen.

 Educator Tips
The educator may also ask how many books would be needed to show how many sperm are available at one ejaculation. (200 - 500 million) Discussion should evolve to how many sperm are necessary for conception (one).

Match It!

Subject: Reproductive Anatomy
Target Population: Students of all ages
Suitable For: Males, females, co-ed groups, parent attended classes
Props Needed: An assortment of items that approximate reproductive organs in size:
> A small section of linguine for fallopian tubes
> A pear for uterus
> An almond for an ovary
> A chart or handout of various sizes and types of fruits that approximate the growing fetus
> A six inch ruler
> A tray
> Cards
> Charts of intrauterine fetal growth
> Chalkboard, flip chart, or wipe off board

Time: Approximately 5 minutes

OVERVIEW
The Match It Game seeks to make the abstract concepts of reproductive organs already introduced in class more concrete.

BEHAVIORAL OBJECTIVES
At the end of the game, the participants will be able to:
◆ Identify relative sizes of reproductive organs
◆ Discuss society's perception of penile size and manhood

PREPARATION - "Setting the Stage"
Prepare a tray with various items analogous in size to reproductive organs. Cards with the names of the organs should be made and placed on a the table.

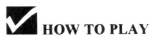 **HOW TO PLAY**

Play of the Game
Items analogous in size to various reproductive organs are arranged on a tray. Students are asked to guess which item is similar in size to which organ on the cards and match it.

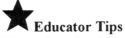 **Educator Tips**
Discussion should lend itself easily to changes in the size of the fetus. The reality of female reproductive organs being "hidden" and therefore difficult for young girls to understand can be introduced. Discussion on the connection between manhood and penile size can be quite interesting: no one is interested, for example, in the size of a young woman's ovaries, but the size of a maturing male's penis is often a matter of concern.

Puzzle It

Subject: Awareness of individual physical changes during puberty
Target Population: Works best with late elementary and middle school students, although may be successfully used at the secondary school level as well
Suitable For: Males, females or co-ed groups
Props Needed: Pictures prepared as puzzles (see Preparation)
                 Magazines
                 Scissors
                 Kitchen timers

                             Time: Approximately 15 minutes

OVERVIEW

Puzzle It focuses upon the individual differences inherent in normal growth and development. It can be used to introduce the concept of normalcy as unique to each young person. The game can be enlarged upon to include discussion of gender representation in the media and the exploitation of pre-pubertal youth.

BEHAVIORAL OBJECTIVES

At the end of the game, the participants will be able to:

◆ Demonstrate skills of puzzle making as a learning tool
◆ Discuss normal changes of puberty within a wide individual variation

---

PREPARATION - "Setting the Stage"
Prepare several magazine pictures of young people in various stages of physical development. Be careful to represent all races and both genders. After mounting the pictures on cardboard and laminating, puzzle pieces should be cut carefully to allow for relative ease in re-figuring. Each puzzle is placed in a plastic ziploc bag for distribution in class. **Give participants the right to "Pass."**

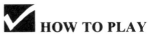 HOW TO PLAY

Play of the Game
Puzzles are distributed to students group in pairs or small groups. One student is selected as the goalkeeper: it is his or her job to set the timer for 2 minutes and monitor puzzle progress. The game begins at a set time. The first group to finish their puzzle wins. Discussion on individual differences is conducted in the small groups with a summary at the end by the educator. Students should answer the questions: How old does the young person in the picture appear to be? What stage of development do you think he or she has reached? How can you tell? Can you see any differences between two males of the same general age in the pictures? Any similarities? How about of females? Are the secondary sexual characteristics more pronounced in males or females?

 Educator Tips
Directed discussion to the labels society and the media assign to "bodies" instead of to people can lead to in-depth conversations among groups. As always, model respect of others.

Sex Ed Dominos

Subject: Setting limits and recognition of consequences
Target Population: Middle school and secondary school level
Suitable For: Males, females or co-ed groups
Props Needed: Empty audiocassette or videocassette cases
Cards (as below)

Time: Approximately 15 minutes

OVERVIEW

The Sex Ed Dominos Game seeks to connect behavior that may lead up to sexual intercourse with the consequences of early sexual activity.

BEHAVIORAL OBJECTIVES

At the end of the game, the participants will be able to:

♦   State the connection between "making out" and possible sex
♦   Discuss setting limits in sexual situations

PREPARATION - "Setting the Stage"
Prepare cards as follows:
*   Talking with someone you like
*   Talking on the phone
*   Being alone with someone
*   Holding hands
*   Kissing
*   French (open mouth) kissing
*   Touching ("feeling someone up")
*   Drinking alcohol
Tape the cards to the empty cassette boxes (choose the size you want for your needs) and stand the boxes on their ends.

 HOW TO PLAY

Play of the Game

Students are divided into small groups. Each group is given a set of "dominos" and told to align them in a row, from least risky to most risky. Discussion should revolve around setting limits and communication wishes.

Educator Tips

Stress to students that their partner may have a different agenda than they think.   Discuss the unspoken messages certain activities give, including dress and friends a student "hangs" with. With secondary school students, you may want to add several cards and dominos to reflect decisions that must be made when students are already sexually active.   Be certain to emphasize that sex doesn't "just happen."

"Birth Parent" for this game = Mary Jo Podgurski, RNC, MA, FACCE

Talk with Me (Parent/Youth Version)

Subject: Communication skills
Target Population: Middle school students and their parents
Suitable For: Males, females or co-ed groups
Props Needed: Two phones per group
Scenario cards

Time: Approximately 15 minutes

OVERVIEW
This version of *Talk with Me* is a role play that encourages positive communication between young people and their parents or guardians.

BEHAVIORAL OBJECTIVES
At the end of the game, the participants will be able to:
♦ Demonstrate positive communication skills when using a phone
♦ State three benefits of keeping communication lines open between parent and child as adolescent begins

PREPARATION - "Setting the Stage"
Prepare scenario cards that focus upon the parent/child relationship. The following scenarios should serve as a catalyst for others that are tailored to your client base:
Scenario:
Youth: You are a 12 year old. You are calling your parent from your friend's houses after school to ask if you may sleepover (it's a Friday night). Your friend wants you to lie to your parents about the evening's activities by telling them you intend to go to the movies. In reality, your friend's parents won't be home and a party is planned. You're uneasy about lying, but don't want to appear to be. You also want to remain at your friend's house. Try to talk your parent into letting you stay. How do you communicate your uneasiness and confusion to your parent with your friend standing right beside you as you call? What would be a safer way to handle this situation and phone call?

Parent: You are uncomfortable with this request. What questions do you ask your child? How do you convey your concerns without alienating your son or daughter? What is your final decision?

 HOW TO PLAY
Play of the Game
Phones and cards are distributed to participants in small groups. After the role play, an evaluation is done within the group and in the class as a whole

 **Educator Tips**
Phones allow for easier role play and permit less inhibited discussion. Evaluation should involve discussion on what the child really wanted, as well as parental needs and expectations.

So.... What Do You Want To Do?

Subject: Decision making skills
Target Population: Middle school students
Suitable For: Males, females or co-ed groups
Props Needed: Video tape jackets of popular movies
Handout of decision making skills
Flip chart, chalkboard, or wipe off board
VCR and TV (optional)

Time: Approximately 15 minutes

OVERVIEW
Good decision making skills are a vital aspect of healthy behavior. This role play models positive decision making in a non-threatening topic familiar to all students.

BEHAVIORAL OBJECTIVES
At the end of the game, the participants will be able to:
♦   List the steps necessary in making a good decision
♦   Demonstrate a healthy decision making process

PREPARATION - "Setting the Stage"
Make a poster or write on the board the steps to making a healthy decision:
Know the facts
Think about the facts
Ask for help if you need it
Act on your decision
Re-wind - re-think your decision
Purchase or borrow several video jackets of different movies that are currently popular.

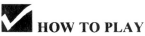 **HOW TO PLAY**

Play of the Game
Students are divided into small groups. After initial discussion on decision making steps, display the video cases and assign the group the decision to rent a movie. Take the group through the decision making process as they rent the film. Evaluate the choice after viewing a few moments of the chosen movie. Would they rent the film at home and finish watching it? Have they ever made the wrong decision and rented a movie that wasn't worth the rental cost? What are the implications of making a wrong decision when the decision involves sexual involvement?

Educator Tips
Students relate well to the video choices. Making the analogy to sexual issues isn't difficult, but may cause some concern to students who have made the wrong decision in the past. Remember to model respect and encourage private communication after class. Reinforce that past decisions are over and behavior we're not proud of should be forgiven. Stress that the next decision made will be a better one.

"Birth Parent" for this game = Mary Jo Podgurski, RNC, MA, FACCE

What Part of No Didn't You Understand?

Subject: Refusal skills
Target Population: Middle school students
Suitable For: Males, females or co-ed groups
Props Needed: Different types of cereal (the weirder, the better)
Plastic cups
Flip chart, chalkboard, or wipe off board

Time: Approximately 30 minutes

OVERVIEW

Refusal skills are a fundamental aspect of postponing sexual involvement, but are often taught in such a formal, preaching fashion that young people "turn off" the message. This role play demonstrate refusal skills using a common everyday item - breakfast cereal. Transference of the refusal skills to more serious subjects follows.

BEHAVIORAL OBJECTIVES

At the end of the game, the participants will be able to:

♦   List four ways to say NO

♦   Demonstrate refusal skills

PREPARATION - "Setting the Stage"
Make a handout or poster or write on the board the following refusal skills:
Ways to say NO:

1. Say No	6. Return the Challenge
2. Ignore the Suggestion	7. Talk about How you Feel
3. Change the Subject	8. Think of Something Better to Do
4. Laugh about Something Else	9. Get Outta There
5. Act Shocked	10. Do Something Else

Make a card with each of these ten items on the front and an explanation on the back
Purchase several brands of breakfast cereal and pour small amounts into plastic cups

---

 HOW TO PLAY

Play of the Game
Students are divided into small groups. After initial discussion on refusal skills, choose one student to try to convince the others in the group to sample a new, strange cereal. Have different students model the different refusal skills necessary in saying NO.

Educator Tips
Students relate well to breakfast cereal choices as an example of refusal skills. Making the analogy to sexual issues isn't difficult, but may cause some concern to students who have made the wrong decision in the past. As always, remember to model respect and encourage private communication after class. Reinforce that past decisions are over and behavior we're not proud of should be forgiven. Stress that the next decision made will be a better one.

Talk with Me (Youth to Youth Version)

Subject: Communication skills, resisting peer pressure
Target Population: Middle school students
Suitable For: Males, females or co-ed groups
Props Needed: Two phones per group
Scenario cards

Time: Approximately 15 minutes

OVERVIEW
This version of *Talk with Me* is a role play that encourages positive communication between young people.

BEHAVIORAL OBJECTIVES
At the end of the game, the participants will be able to:
♦   Demonstrate positive communication skills when using a phone
♦   State three benefits of keeping communication lines open as dating relationships begin

---

PREPARATION - "Setting the Stage"
Prepare scenario cards that focus upon early dating scenarios. Include situations that involve parties, drinking, and asking for dates (homecoming, etc) A possible scenario:

Scenario:
Youth: You receive a phone call from a kid you know from the bus ride to and from school. You are very flattered, because this person is popular and looked up to by other students. During the phone call you are invited to a party. Talk on the phone and decide as you speak: Do you accept right away? What kinds of questions should you ask about the party? How will you feel if you decide the party is risky and say no to the invitation?

 HOW TO PLAY

Play of the Game
Phones and cards are distributed to participants in small groups. I usually "play" one phone role, for example, I'll ask the student to go to the party. After the role play, an evaluation is done within the group and in the class as a whole

Educator Tips
Once more, phones allow for easier role play and permit less inhibited discussion. Evaluation should involve discussion on risk and peer pressure.

Balloon Game

Subject: Learning styles
Target Population: Any groups
Suitable For: Males, females or co-ed groups
Props Needed: Red and green Helium filled balloons
    Flip chart, chalkboard, or wipe off board
    Markers

Time: Approximately 10 minutes

OVERVIEW
The Balloon Game allows for group participation while discussing learning styles

BEHAVIORAL OBJECTIVES
At the end of the game, the participants will be able to:
♦ Discuss three types learning styles
♦ Assess themselves for their favorite teaching techniques

PREPARATION - "Setting the Stage"
Prior to the session, the educator should prepare Helium filled balloons in red and green colors. There should be a red and a green balloon for each participant.

A list of questions to help participants assess their own learning style should be prepared as well. These questions should require Yes or No answers and may include:

Do you enjoy role play?
Do you like to take notes?
Would you prefer attending a lecture? etc.

 HOW TO PLAY
Play of the Game
After discussion of learning styles, the educator should read the list of questions. Participants will vote "Yes" or "No" by raising the red or green balloon. (Red for no, green for yes)

Educator Tips
Remember that some learners will hate this exercise! Your last question should be: Did you like playing this game?

Chapter Five
Games for Sexuality Education

*We are now at a point where
we must educate our children in
what no one knew yesterday,
and prepare our schools
for what no one knows yet*

.... Margaret Mead

Risk Card Game

Subject*:* Risks associated with sexual activity
Target Population: Middle and high school students
Suitable For: Males, females or co-ed groups
Props Needed*:* Seven color of 3" by 3" cut cards
                              Post- it notes in a contrasting color
                              Pencils, paper

                                        Time: Approximately 40 minutes

OVERVIEW
Risk Card Game is an high level experiential game that really hits home with teens. Although complicated it is well worth the effort, since young people consistently "get it" at the end of the game.

BEHAVIORAL OBJECTIVES
At the end of the game, the participants will:
♦ Identify three risks associated with sexual activity
♦ Recognize the ease of STD and HIV/AIDS transmission
♦ Discuss abstinence as a choice
♦ Role play refusal skills

PREPARATION - "Setting the Stage"
• Prepare 3 x 3 colored cards in the following proportions:

20% Pink and Red (40%)	Signify HIV or AIDS
20% Green and Orange (40%)	Signify Condom Use or Abstinence
10% Blue and White (20%)	Signify IV Drug Use or Chlamydia
2 yellow cards	

• Attach post-it notes to each of the cards
• Sign educator's name to the post-it notes on the yellow cards
• Prepare two 5 X 8 cards that read "I Pass"
• Explain Play of the Game carefully to students

 HOW TO PLAY

Play of the Game

Phase One: Preliminary Questions
Prior to trading cards ask each student to write answers to the following four questions on a sheet of paper (scrap paper will do) Stress the fact that these answers are for the student's eyes only: the paper will not be collected or examined in any way.

             Please write your *favorite food*
             Please write the name of your *favorite person*
             Please write your *favorite activity*
             Please write a *secret* you want no one to know, and circle it
             (Note: Explain that an actual secret may seem too "dangerous" to write down,
             and the student may prefer to simply place an empty circle on the paper)

Phase Two: Trading Cards

- Students select six (6) cards of one color from a pile at the front of the room. After they return to their seats, they write their names (first and last if the class is unfamiliar with each other) on the post-it notes attached to EACH card. Any names that are already on the Post-it notes should be crossed out.
- Students are then instructed to exchange cards with other students in the room with the following ground rules:
  1. The educator assigns a color (one of the 20% proportion colors) which will be abstinent. That terminology should be avoided, however, at the start of the trading. Students should simply be instructed that the holder of that color may not trade. For example: "Today, blue may not trade."
  2. No one is forced to trade
  3. Although force is never allowed, bribery is acceptable!
  4. The instructor begins the trade by exchanging his/her yellow cards with two students
  5. Trade should last 5 minutes. Any color combination is acceptable

Phase Three: Putting It All Together

After the trade is completed, student should return to their seats. The educator then asks the two students he/she originally traded with to rise and read the names written on their cards. As each student's name is read, that student should also stand. Eventually, everyone will be standing except the students who didn't trade. **The educator should then reveal the meaning of the cards' colors.** In order for a student to remain uninfected in the game, he/she must:

NOT TRADE (Remaining abstinent)

Have ONE MORE condom colored card than HIV or AIDS cards

(since condoms don't work 100% of the time)

Phase Four: Re-cap

The students should finally be instructed to return to the questions they originally answered in Phase One of the game. Those who were infected MUST completed this part of the game. The students' choices are erased from their papers in turn, with AIDS related rationale for their removal:

  1. *Favorite food* - rationale - Can someone eat well with oral Herpes?
  2. *Favorite person* - rationale - How would this person react to HIV positive news? Would the reaction be different if the person chosen was a sexual partner?
  3. *Favorite activity* - rationale - Could someone still enjoy this if ill?
  4. *Secret* - rationale - Erase the circle, because the secret is revealed. (Many secrets are sexual in nature, and would be revealed with testing)

 Educator Tips

If teaching in a school, the meaning of the colors should be varied with every new class. Be careful to model respect and dignity for people living with AIDS, and differentiate HIV infection as different from AIDS status. It is vital that this game be played with the proper attitude - avoidance of risk is a healthy choice, but those infected are not to be avoided or feared.

As time permits, the educator should initiate open discussion on:
- Your true "sex partner" group in terms of contagion
- Decision making and refusal skills needed to remain abstinent
- Peer pressure (often students who aren't permitted to trade will gather together)

What's THAT got to do with IT?

Subject: Myths and misinformation about sex and conception
Target Population: Middle and secondary school students
Suitable For: Males, females or co-ed groups
Props Needed: Cards

Time: Approximately one class room period of 40 or 45 minutes

OVERVIEW
What's THAT got to do with IT? can easily serve as an initial game in a sexuality education program. It is an excellent icebreaker with new students as well as a way for the educator to ascertain the knowledge base of the students.

BEHAVIORAL OBJECTIVES
At the end of the game, the participants will:
♦ Begin to differentiate between myths, misinformation and fact regarding sexual issues

---

PREPARATION - "Setting the Stage"
Print the words below on cards - preferably on large, brightly colored card stock. Laminate if possible, to preserve from wear and tear. I use standard 8 1/2 by 11 paper, cut in half. The words should be easily visible from across the room.

Period, "Do It", "Making Love", Pull Out, Kinds, Stand up, Douche, Water, Orgasm, First Time, Safe Time, Seven Years, Mountain Dew, Hot, Winter, No Way, NO!, Maybe, I Don't Know, Not Me, Jacuzzi. Five Days, Why Me? It Just Happened, "Safe sex?"
(In conservative schools, or with in-experienced students, you may want to eliminate the cards Pull Out, Orgasm, Kinds, Douche)

 HOW TO PLAY

Play of the Game
Each student chooses a card from the pile. He or she reads the word on the pile, and the class brainstorms the possible connection that word or phrase could have with sex. The educator explains the cards.

 Educator Tips
Explain that no one will be forced to participate. No one will be made to explain the meanings of the words on the cards, that's the educator's job. Anyone may ask questions, answer questions, or make comments at any time, but only one person at a time may speak. Everyone in the room will be respectful of all others. No racist or homophobic remarks will be allowed. Remember the tone of your remarks - convey that there is no 100% safe sex by your answers and comments. Be as non-judgmental as possible. The cards all relate to myths regarding sexual activity. For example, Mountain Dew is supposed to lower sperm count, you can make a baby in the water or in a Jacuzzi, a student told me that a girl is a virgin again if she doesn't have sex again for seven years, etc.

Grab Bag Game - Prevention

Subject: Prevention of pregnancy, STD's and HIV/AIDS
Target Population: Secondary school students
Suitable For: Males, females or co-ed groups
Props Needed: Lunch bags
                 Contraceptive and disease prevention devices
                 Cards as below

Time: Approximately 40 minutes

OVERVIEW
The Grab Bag Game focuses upon prevention of pregnancy, sexually transmitted diseases, and HIV/AIDS. It should be presented after lessons a solid foundation of decision making and refusal skills as well as a mini lecture on contraception.

BEHAVIORAL OBJECTIVES
At the end of the game, the participants will:
♦ Acknowledge abstinence as the only 100% safe sex
♦ Discuss reasons students choose to become sexually active
♦ List two contraceptive devices most likely to provide protection

---

PREPARATION - "Setting the Stage"
Prior to the session, the educator should place various contraceptive devices into the lunch bags.
Cards should be prepared with the following words:
No, Love, Trust, Honesty, Please God, and Hope
The cards should also be placed in the bags.

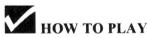 **HOW TO PLAY**

Play of the Game
Students each select a bag - be respectful of "I Pass" - and open the bags, one at a time. If a student is reluctant to explore the contents of the bag, it may be handed to the educator to open and discuss. Students who wish to do so may touch and examine the devices.

Educator Tips
It is vital that discussion regarding prevention issues, abstinence as a 100% safe choice, and decision making, refusal skills be presented prior to this playing this game.

Open discussion should evolve regarding the words on the cards:
What do those things have to do with sexual activity?
Can they protect a person from risk?
What affect does love, hope, trust, etc, have on prevention of pregnancy or diseases?

Madison Avenue "Sell It" Game

Subject: Messages hidden in advertising campaigns
Target Population: Middle or secondary school students
Suitable For: Males, females or co-ed groups
Props Needed: Magazine pictures of current sales campaigns (recognizable to students)
                    Slides of magazine pictures

Time: Approximately 20 minutes

OVERVIEW

The Madison Avenue "Sell It" Game addresses the underlying messages in advertising. Exploitation of pre-pubescent persons of both persons, sexuality as a sub-conscious sales technique, pressure to use cigarettes and alcohol, and eating disorders are examined.

BEHAVIORAL OBJECTIVES

At the end of the game, the participants will:

♦ State the hidden messages behind ad campaigns

♦ Assess the influence of these messages upon consumers

♦ Discuss the groups reaction to the advertisements

♦ Demonstrate decision making skills necessary to resist pressure

---

PREPARATION - "Setting the Stage"

Prior to the session, the educator should prepare slides made from advertising campaigns, looking for pictures that show the following:

* Pre-pubescent young people in adult situations (embracing, standing in an erotic position)
* Half clothed models
* Erotic pictures that sell items not normally associated with sex - for e.g., jeans ads with no jeans
* Overly thin models
* Models with blank expressions
* Models where the female is portrayed in a bondage situation or appears fearful
* Young appearing models in ads for cigarettes and alcohol
* Torsos without faces

Current magazines should be distributed to the class for discussion as well

---

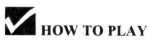 **HOW TO PLAY**

Play of the Game

The class should be divided into small groups to permit open discussion.

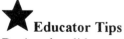**Educator Tips**

During the slide presentation, the students may discuss the following questions within their group:
What is the ad trying to sell us?   What is the underlying message it conveys?
How can pressure of this nature be withstood?   Does society have an obligation to regulate ads?
What message does the ad convey regarding women, children's bodies, respect for personhood?

Dating Contract Game

Subject: Interpersonal relationships
Target Population: Middle or secondary school students
Suitable For: Males, females or co-ed groups (co-ed groups preferred)
Props Needed: Chalkboard or wipe off board
         Timer

Time: Approximately 15 minutes

OVERVIEW
The Dating Contract Game examines the reality of interpersonal relationships among young people. Students are asked to consider their expectations when entering into a new relationship.

BEHAVIORAL OBJECTIVES
At the end of the game, the participants will be able to:
♦ Discuss the relative readiness of their age group for dating
♦ List 6 positive attributes for a dating relationship
♦ Role play communication skills needed to convey the need for this contract to a partner

---

PREPARATION - "Setting the Stage"
A handout on dating or an actual contract may be prepared prior to the session.
Ideally this game should follow discussion on decision making and peer pressure

---

 HOW TO PLAY

Play of the Game
Divide the class into small groups. Choose a discussion leader. The educator sets the timer for 5 minutes. During that time, the group must create a dating contract, that is, a list of positive things necessary for a good dating relationship. When the timer rings, the group must stop discussion, no matter how sparse their list is.

Educator Tips
The addition of the timer to an otherwise bland exercise adds some excitement and has an underlying educational component. Students should only be told that they must hurry in their discussion. At the end of the time, each group leader will read the group's list aloud. The educator should write each new contract attribute on the board. Discussion should then move to the difficulty some groups had coming up with the contracts in a short time. This can be an excellent springboard for the fact that most young people enter into dating relationships without any forethought, not even the five minutes allotted in this game.

What's Love Got to Do with It? Part 1

Subject: Different types of love
Target Population: Middle or secondary school students
Suitable For: Males, females or co-ed groups
Props Needed: Chalkboard or wipe off board

Time: Approximately 15 minutes

OVERVIEW
The What's Love Got to Do with It? Part One Game discusses love as a powerful human emotion that has different meanings dependent upon the situation.

BEHAVIORAL OBJECTIVES
At the end of the game, the participants will be able to:

♦ List three types of love

♦ Describe a situation where one type of love can evolve into another

---

PREPARATION - "Setting the Stage"
Prior to the session, the educator should write the following words on the board:
PUPPY LOVE OR INFATUATION
ROMANTIC LOVE
SEXUAL LOVE
LOVE BETWEEN FRIENDS
PARENTAL LOVE
SIBLING LOVE
LOVE FOR A PET
LOVE FOR A SONG, MUSIC GROUP, ETC.
LOVE FOR COUNTRY OR STATE
LOVE OF GOD
LOVE AS SEEN IN THE MEDIA
MATURE LOVE
IMMATURE LOVE

 **HOW TO PLAY**
Play of the Game
Students are chosen to write at the board. The entire group gives examples of the different types of love written above.

Educator Tips
Discussion should bring up the following points:
Love is everywhere - what makes it so powerful? Can a person love someone in one way and have that love change over time? How is love portrayed in the media? Is that a realistic portrayal? *What's Love Got to Do with It Part Two* should follow.

What's Love Got to Do with It? Part 2

Subject: Connection between love and lust
Target Population: Middle or secondary school students
Suitable For: Males, females or co-ed groups
Props Needed: Three jars labeled: Love, Lust, Garbage Lines
Cards as below

Time: Approximately 15 minutes

OVERVIEW
The What's Love Got to Do with It? Part Two Game focuses upon the difference between love and lust. It attempts to differentiate those two powerful feelings without passing judgment on youth for experiencing either of them.

BEHAVIORAL OBJECTIVES
At the end of the game, the participants will:
♦   Evaluate "lines" for love vs lust as a motivate
♦   Discuss different agendas in the minds of partners

PREPARATION - "Setting the Stage"
Prior to the session, the educator should prepare cards with "lines" that both genders may use in a dating situation. Examples are:
Let's talk about sex
What do you want to do Friday night?
I don't think we're ready for sex
Hey, do you want to hear what we did last night?
Did you catch her/his body?
He/she is hot!
I love you
My parents aren't home Friday night. Do you want to come over?
Labels should be placed on three clear plastic jars: LOVE, LUST, GARBAGE LINES

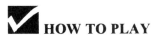 **HOW TO PLAY**
Play of the Game
Each student chooses a card and places it in the appropriate jar. Garbage lines refer to statements that are less than truthful and are said only to coerce someone into something.

Educator Tips
Discussion should evolve into using others and setting limits in a relationship. Small group work on the concepts of trust may follow. Lust should not be dismissed as an alien or evil feeling, but rather should be accepted as a normal course of an adolescent's life. Being able to differentiate love from lust is important, however, as well as recognizing that feeling lust doesn't mean acting upon it.

The "Sex Lady's" Top Ten #1

Subject: Reasons to postpone sex
Target Population: Middle or secondary school students
Suitable For: Males, females or co-ed groups
Props Needed: Chalkboard, wipe off board or flip chart
                  Writing utensils - chalk or markers

Time: Approximately 10 minutes

OVERVIEW
The "Sex Lady's" Top Ten Game is a play on the top ten list of late night TV. Students develop the list in class, and have a chance to work through reasons for postponing sex as they do so.

BEHAVIORAL OBJECTIVES
At the end of the game, the participants will:

♦ List ten reasons for postponing sex

PREPARATION - "Setting the Stage"
Prior to the session, the educator may want to develop a list of reasons to fall back on if discussion slows.

 HOW TO PLAY

Play of the Game
Choose a student to write on the board. Discussion should revolve around ten reasons to remain abstinent and postpone sexual involvement.

 Educator Tips
Remember to reinforce the concept of healthy decision making and reducing risk. Students who have been sexually active in the past should still consider postponing sex if the situation is risky or if they are not comfortable with the situation. (Students call me the "Sex Lady" - not type casting, but the "label" has stuck!)

The "Sex Lady's " Top Ten #2

Subject: Top ten desirable traits in a healthy relationship
Target Population: Middle or secondary school students
Suitable For: Males, females or co-ed groups
Props Needed: Chalkboard, wipe off board or flip chart
                Writing utensils - chalk or markers

Time: Approximately 10 minutes

OVERVIEW
The "Sex Lady's" Top Ten Game #2 is a play on the top ten list of late night TV. Students develop the list of traits in a healthy relationship in class, and have a chance to work through issues of love and attraction as they do so.

BEHAVIORAL OBJECTIVES
At the end of the game, the participants will:
♦   List the top ten desirable traits in a partner

PREPARATION - "Setting the Stage"
Prior to the session, the educator may want to develop a list of reasons to fall back on if discussion slows.

 HOW TO PLAY
Play of the Game
Choose a student to write on the board. Discussion should revolve around the top ten items in a healthy relationship

Educator Tips
Discuss the reality of attraction as a fleeting thing when people are young. Draw analogies to students change in taste in music, food, and clothes over the last five years. A significant change in preferences may follow as they reach adulthood as well. Pausing to think about what we want in a relationship is both healthy and decreases risky behavior

Fly Away

Subject: Sexual issues and risk taking
Target Population: Secondary school students
Suitable For: Males, females or co-ed groups
Props Needed: Chalkboard, wipe off board or flip chart
Paper airplanes (see preparation)

Time: Approximately 40 minutes

OVERVIEW
The Fly Away Game is a unique vehicle that reinforces decreasing risk and healthy sexual decision making.

BEHAVIORAL OBJECTIVES
At the end of the game, the participants will be able to:
♦ Review sexual decision making
♦ Review steps needed to reduce risk

PREPARATION - "Setting the Stage"
Prior to the session, the educator should create paper airplanes (unfolded) with questions written on them. These questions may include:
* The number of persons infected with AIDS in your area
* Condoms + Vaseline = ?
* Is oral sex safe?
* What is the percentage of student in your grade level that you think is sexually active?
* Is it OK to remain a virgin at your age?
* What are some reasons to wait?
* Teen pregnancy rate in your area

 HOW TO PLAY
Play of the Game
Each student chooses a flat paper airplane to construct. When the planes are finished, the students sit in a circle. They then propel their airplanes towards another student one at a time. The student who receives the airplane opens it and answers the question, or comments upon the topic.

Educator Tips
Students may work in small groups or singly, as they prefer. Be watchful that the situation doesn't escalate - one student should propel his/her plane at a time!!

Music Rules

Subject: Media messages about sexuality
Target Population: Secondary school students
Suitable For: Males, females or co-ed groups
Props Needed: Chalkboard, wipe off board or flip chart
                    CD or tape player
                    Current CD's and tapes

Time: Approximately 40 minutes

OVERVIEW
The Music Rules Game is both current and popular. It focuses on the messages in current music and assists with dealing with pressure associated with those messages.

BEHAVIORAL OBJECTIVES
At the end of the game, the participants will be able to:
♦ List messages in current music
♦ Discuss the influence that music gives to young people

PREPARATION - "Setting the Stage"
Prior to the session, the educator should prepare a handout on the music. The handout should have room for the title of the piece and student comments.

The music chosen should be current and should provide impetus for discussion on the following points:
*   The image the music provides of sex
*   The message behind the music
*   Gender stereotypes
*   Influence of the music upon youth

 HOW TO PLAY
Play of the Game
Small groups are formed to allow for discussion. The music is played by the educator while each group listens and then discusses the piece. A discussion leader shares the groups impressions after each selection.

Educator Tips
Examples of excellent music for this exercise are:
Tina Turner's *What's Love Got to Do with It?*
Reba McEntire's *She Thinks His Name Is John*
Seasons of Love from the Rent soundtrack

The "Who am I?" Journal

Subject: Gender stereotypes
Target Population: Secondary school students
Suitable For: Males, females or co-ed groups
Props Needed: Chalkboard, wipe off board or flip chart
                Journal entrees (as below)

Time: Approximately 20 minutes

OVERVIEW
The "Who am I?" Journal Game directs student attention to gender stereotypes and society's expectations of male and female roles.

BEHAVIORAL OBJECTIVES
At the end of the game, the participants will be able to:
♦   Discuss gender stereotypes in society today
♦   Brainstorm ways to permit choices to both genders and avoid stereotypes

---

PREPARATION - "Setting the Stage"
Prior to the session, the educator should prepare beginning journal entries. An example of such entries are:
*   Who am I?
I enjoy staying at home with my young son. We throw ball together, enjoy hiking, and shoot hoops
*   Who am I?
I made an appointment at the clinic to get birth control?
*   Who am I?
I'm a professional athlete making a million dollars a year
*   Who am I?
I was just diagnosed with HIV/AIDS

 **HOW TO PLAY**
Play of the Game
Students in small groups should take a beginning journal entry and enlarge upon it, being careful not to reveal the gender of journal owner. Each group reads their completed journal and the class discusses the probable gender of the writer.

**Educator Tips**
Students can really have fun with this concept.   Monitor their level of involvement and model respect for all people.

"Sex = Serious" Game

Subject: Consequences of sex
Target Population: Middle or secondary school students
Suitable For: Males, females or co-ed groups
Props Needed: Chalkboard, wipe off board or flip chart
                Pictures of fetal development in utero
                Sex = serious worksheet
                Empathy Belly

Time: Approximately 20 minutes

OVERVIEW
The Sex = Serious Game addresses childbearing as a consequence of sexual activity

BEHAVIORAL OBJECTIVES
At the end of the game, the participants will be able to:

♦ Discuss the connection between sexual activity and early childbearing
♦ List three serious consequences early sexual activity
♦ Demonstrate use of the Empathy Belly (optional, only if students volunteer)

PREPARATION - "Setting the Stage"
Prior to the session, the educator should prepare a handout for small group work asking the group to respond the following questions:

What are three things that can happen to a person who has sex?
What are three ways that a young person's life would be different if a they (or they're partner) become pregnant?
Is Sex Serious? How would YOUR life change if you were a parent?
List three things that you did yesterday that would have to be different if your were the mother or father of a baby.

 HOW TO PLAY

Play of the Game
Students should be divided into groups for discussion. A group leader should be chosen. During discussion for each question, students will talk among themselves, and report to the group as a whole. After each question is discussed, a new student may try on the Empathy Belly.

Educator Tips
Be serious with demonstration of the Empathy Belly. Model respect for women as you use the visual aids to describe interior physical changes during pregnancy.

Label Game

Subject: Labels or stereotypes assigned to groups
Target Population: Middle or secondary school students
Suitable For: Males, females or co-ed groups
Props Needed: Chalkboard, wipe off board or flip chart
　　　　　　　　Writing utensils - chalk or markers
　　　　　　　　Post-it notes with labels pre-written on them
　　　　　　　　Three cans or packages of consumer goods one each with:
　　　　　　　　　　Clear packaging: for e.g., a jar of peanut butter
　　　　　　　　　　Opaque packaging: for e.g., a can of soup
　　　　　　　　　　Altered contents: for e.g., a clear jar of beets containing pickles
　　　　　　　　　　　　　　　　　　Time: Approximately 20 minutes

OVERVIEW
The Label Game addresses societal expectations for gender as well as the stereotypes peers label each other with. It is an excellent vehicle for modeling tolerance as well as a springboard for discussion of drug and alcohol use, risky behavior, and consequences of sex

BEHAVIORAL OBJECTIVES
At the end of the game, the participants will be able to:
♦ Discuss the use of gender labels in association with sexuality
♦ Evaluate the effect drugs and alcohol have on sexual acting out
♦ Assess the behavior of the "couple" for healthy decision making

---

PREPARATION - "Setting the Stage"
Prior to the session, the educator should prepare stick up notes (for example Post-it brand) with the following labels:

Slut	Easy	Stud	Babe	Fast	Lucky
Loose	Puts Out	Irresponsible	Macho	Scored	Bad Reputation,
Give it Up	"Ho"	"The Man"	Mother	Father	HIV positive - 2

 HOW TO PLAY
Play of the Game
Two student volunteers are asked to draw a male and female figure on the board. A mini-discussion regarding labeling should occur while the artists work. Discussion should touch on labels as trustworthy, as false advertising, and as assigned capriciously.

When the drawings are compete, the educator describes a scenario where these two students - choose age and grade with care - meet for the first time at a party, get drunk and have sex. The next day they return to school. How would they be greeted by their fellow students? Members of the class are given all of the post-it notes except "Mother," "Father," and the two "HIV Positives," Students should then stick the labels on the gender image where they think such a label would normally be assigned by peers.

**Educator Tips**

Asking students to initiate this game by drawing a male and female figure on the board should be done with caution. Remember to set parameters for the figures if you desire. You can be certain that a few students will make their "male" and "female" graphic in ways the you may not have considered.

Discussion of reputation, difficulty correcting bad reputations, rumors, and labels "sticking" in spite of future behavior, should all be addressed.

After discussion of gender stereotypes, ask the group if the students have taken other risks beyond the risk to their reputations. Mother and Father cards can now be added to the figures. Finally, add the HIV post-its and discuss ways to decrease risk of disease.

Match Game

Subject: Sexual decision making and risk taking
Target Population: Secondary school students
Suitable For: Males, females or co-ed groups
Props Needed: Chalkboard, wipe off board or flip chart
          Magazines
          Scissors
          Match cards (see below)

Time: Approximately 20 minutes

OVERVIEW
The Match Game focuses upon two concepts: Media influence on sexuality, and the consequences of actions.

BEHAVIORAL OBJECTIVES
At the end of the game, the participants will be able to:

♦ Discuss the ways media influence our standards sexually

♦ List three consequences early sexual activity

PREPARATION - "Setting the Stage"

Prior to the session, the educator should prepare match cards using words, phrases and pictures from popular magazines. Pictures and phrases should be mounted on three different colors of paper as follows:

Color A (Red) is the "come on" - the advertising hook
Color B (White) is the action - what the picture inspires one to do
Color C (Blue) is the consequence of the action
Examples of match cards are:
A (Red) = A picture of a man and a woman kissing - phrase "Oh, baby, baby, baby"
B (White) = A picture of a man and a women lying in bed together
C (Blue) = A picture of a baby "Oh, baby, baby, baby"
Students should be encouraged to create their own match cards using the magazines and scissors.

 **HOW TO PLAY**

Play of the Game
Students may participate in two ways: First, they may match the cards and discuss the media message and the consequences of the actions they inspire, and Second, they may divide into small groups and create their own match cards

 **Educator Tips**
Be cognizant of the message you give with pictures. Model diversity respectfully and be certain that your pictures represent all races - the face of America

Didja Catch that Line?

Subject: Pressure lines
Target Population: Middle or secondary school students
Suitable For: Males, females or co-ed groups
Props Needed: Cards as below

Time: Approximately 35 minutes

OVERVIEW
The Didja Catch that Line? Game is an excellent vehicle for discussing pressure and setting limits.

BEHAVIORAL OBJECTIVES
At the end of the game, the participants will:
- Evaluate the pressure lines for sincerity
- Demonstrate communication skills necessary for setting limits

---

PREPARATION - "Setting the Stage"
Prior to the session, the educator should prepare cards with pressure lines. Examples are:
If you won't have sex with me, then someone else will
Everybody's doing it.
Don't worry, I'll be careful
I can't stop!!
Come on, take a drink. It will get you in the mood
I'll always be there for you
It's my first time too
I'll never pressure you
I'll wait as long as you want
Don't tell your parents
There's never been anyone else for me but you
I love you
I love you, too

 HOW TO PLAY

Play of the Game
Students choose a card and read the line aloud. Discussion revolves around the line - is it believable, is it real, has anyone heard it?
Students then divide into pairs and role play setting limits in response to the lines.

Educator Tips
Dividing the groups into pairs will help eliminate the feeling of being "on stage" that may occur is the role play portion of this game were done in the main group. Monitor student dyads carefully to assure their continued interaction in the game when subdivided, however, since two students working alone may easily become distracted

Well, it's Done Now!

Subject: Virginity
Target Population: Middle or secondary school students
Suitable For: Males, females or co-ed groups
Props Needed: Chalkboard, wipe off board or flip chart

Time: Approximately 10 minutes

OVERVIEW
The Well, It's Done Now Game addresses the issue of virginity as a concept. Students are asked to examine the possibility that persons of worth are both virgins and non-virgins, and that sexual decision making should be well thought out, not a matter of habit.

BEHAVIORAL OBJECTIVES
At the end of the game, the participants will:
♦ Define virginity
♦ Discuss self-concept
♦ Role play decision making skills

PREPARATION:
Prior to the session, the educator should write on the board:
Virgin
Non-virgin
Cards (enough for each group) should be printed with the following scenario:
A fifteen year old has had sex for the first time.
* If it was a negative experience, does that person still need to continue to have sex?
* If it was a positive experience, are there any reasons why the person should stop and re-think their decision?
* If it was a positive experience, what can the person do to reduce risk?
* Role Play the following: 1. The person tells his/her partner that they shouldn't have sex again
                            2. The person tells his/her partner that they should use protection

---

 HOW TO PLAY
Play of the Game
Students are asked to write words that they associate with virgin and non-virgin on the board. Discussion of gender - is there a different perception with male and female - should be on-going as the words are written. Students should then divide into small groups to role play the scenario

 Educator Tips
Many students feel they have little choice in sexual decision making once they've lost their virginity. This game is an opportunity to dispel that myth and encourage behavior that decreases risk. Discussion may touch on the concept of young people initiating sex to "get it over with."

STD Dress Up

Subject: Sexually transmitted diseases
Target Population: Secondary school students
Suitable For: Males, females or co-ed groups
Props Needed: Chalkboard, wipe off board or flip chart
  Dress up clothes:
    Old hats, gruesome Halloween masks, hair curlers, old jewelry
  Signs as below

Time: Approximately 40 minutes

OVERVIEW
The STD Dress Up Game is a unique way to reinforce information on sexually transmitted diseases.

BEHAVIORAL OBJECTIVES
At the end of the game, the participants will be able to:
♦ Review sexually transmitted diseases that are most common among their age group
♦ Role play the following: severity of disease, connection to sexual activity, ease of transmission

---

PREPARATION:
Prior to the session, the educator should prepare several sets of Descriptive Cards as follows:

Ease of transmission: Easy	Treatable
Ease of transmission: Moderate	Not easily treated
Ease of transmission: Difficult	Sterility
How spread: Sexually	Chronic illness
How spread: Without sex	Death

Signs (to be worn around the student's neck) should be prepared with the names of common sexually transmitted diseases, HIV infection and AIDS

Information sheets on each STD, HIV, and AIDS

 **HOW TO PLAY**
Play of the Game
Students who wish to participate are given a STD identity and information sheet. They are they permitted to choose "dress up" clothes as they like and dress according to their perception of that disease. Hats are especially helpful and fun. Each student then introduces him or herself to the group. The group then evaluates the choice of "dress" and decides upon which Descriptive Cards belong with which disease

 **Educator Tips**
Ideally this game should follow a cognitive session on STD's. If that isn't the case, care should be taken to avoid confusion by moving through the diseases slowly.

Sex Ed Talk Show

Subject: Student opinion about sexual issues
Target Population: Secondary school students
Suitable For: Males, females or co-ed groups
Props Needed: Chalkboard, wipe off board or flip chart
Button that says "Talk Show Host"
Toy microphone
Applause card
Cards as below

Time: Approximately 30 minutes

OVERVIEW
The Sex Ed Talk Show Game is a fun filled game that can really "take off." Student "talk show hosts" lead discussion into current issues regarding sexuality

BEHAVIORAL OBJECTIVES
At the end of the game, the participants will be able to:
♦ Discuss current issues regarding sexuality

PREPARATION - "Setting the Stage"
Prior to the session, the educator should prepare several packages of cards for discussion. Sample topics may be:
* Should condoms be available in schools?
* Does Sex Ed encourage teens to have sex?
* What can be done to encourage young teens to be abstinent?
* If a teen wants to have sex, is there anything an adult can do to stop him or her?
* True or false: Woman have sex for love, men have sex for sex!
* Who is responsible for the baby when a teen gets pregnant: the teen mother or father?
* Who should set limits in a relationship - the man or the woman?
* Is there a double standard in our society for men and women?
* Why are women called "sluts" when they have sex, and men called "studs?"
* How much should society pay to help teen parents raise their babies?

 HOW TO PLAY
Play of the Game
One or two talk show hosts are chosen. In a large group, the remainder of the students can be divided into panel and audience. The "talk show" proceeds as in any current talk show format. Discussion should be paused to allow for audience participation.

 Educator Tips
Allow students to volunteer for the host positions. I've often been pleasantly surprised when a supposedly quiet student took on this role and loved it!

Phone Sex

Subject: Sexual decision making
Target Population: Secondary school students
Suitable For: Males, females or co-ed groups
Props Needed: Chalkboard, wipe off board or flip chart
Phones
Scenario cards (as below)

Time: Approximately 40 minutes

OVERVIEW
The Phone Sex Game addresses sexual decision making utilizing a vehicle that is well known to teens and therefore conducive to role play

BEHAVIORAL OBJECTIVES
At the end of the game, the participants will be able to:
♦ Review sexual decision making
♦ Review steps needed to reduce risk

PREPARATION:
Prior to the session, the educator should prepare scenarios for role play. Examples are:

* Calling the clinic to ask for contraception
* Calling the clinic to ask for an exam
* Calling the clinic to ask for an HIV/AIDS test
* Receiving a phone call from a friend who thinks she may be pregnant
* Receiving a phone call from a past partner who thinks he/she may be infected with an STD
* Receiving a phone call from a past partner who thinks he/she may be infected with HIV

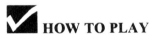 **HOW TO PLAY**

Play of the Game
Students divide into groups and pretend to call each other, acting out the scenario in an impromptu fashion.

 Educator Tips
The educator should model the first phone call. Model the groups carefully to ascertain positive communication skills and healthy decision making. Reinforce abstinence as a choice.

Walkin' Bodies

Subject: Conception anatomy review
Target Population: Secondary school students
Suitable For: Males, females or co-ed groups
Props Needed: Large cards (as below)

Time: Approximately 20 minutes

OVERVIEW
The Walkin' Bodies Game is a quick review anatomy review game that can also be utilized to discuss "safe" times, protection, and decision making

BEHAVIORAL OBJECTIVES
At the end of the game, the participants will be able to:
♦ Identify male and female reproductive anatomy
♦ Review decision making necessary to reduce risk

PREPARATION - "Setting the Stage"
Prior to the session, the educator should prepare large "name" cards as follows:

UTERUS
SPERM
FALLOPIAN TUBE
OVUM
PENIS
CONDOM
SETTING LIMITS
THE "PILL"

 HOW TO PLAY

Play of the Game
Students volunteer to play the role on the cards. The cards should be worn or held by the student. The game begins as we discuss how conception takes place: How much sexual activity has to occur for conception? How close does the sperm need to be to impregnate the woman? Is there an absolutely 100% safe time of the month? etc. Discussion can then move to prevention items: Does the pill protect against disease? How accurate is protection? How can we reduce risk?

 Educator Tips

The educator should model the game by playing the role of the most controversial item - typically the "penis" with a relaxed, yet serious attitude. That will *usually* set the tone for a good learning experience. Know your group - this one isn't for everyone. Watch that the students don't get out of control.

Chapter Six
Games for
Parenting
Education

*A rich child often sits
in a poor mother's lap*

.... Danish Proverb

*One father is more than
a hundred schoolmasters*

.....George Herbert

Read to Me Game

Subject: Encourage literacy
Target Population: New parents, especially young men and women
Suitable For: Males, females or co-ed groups
Props Needed: Selection of children's books
                Handouts
                Flip chart and markers

Time: Approximately 40 minutes

OVERVIEW
The Read to Me Game reinforces reading as an important way to connect with a young child. Exposure to literary experiences at the preschool level can truly give a head start to children.

BEHAVIORAL OBJECTIVES
At the end of the game, the participants will be able to:
♦ Demonstrate read aloud techniques

PREPARATION - "Setting the Stage"
Prior to the session, the educator should prepare handouts on reading to a small child. The handouts should include pictures of small children and the following information:

Read to Me:
* Help make me feel loved - read to me
* Help me grow - read to me
* Help me smile - read to me
* Help me laugh - read to me
* Help me see myself as a great person - read to me
* Help me explore places I've never been - read to me
* Help me understand the world - read to me
* Help me reach out to others - let me read to you
* Help me love you back - let me read to you

Prepare guidelines for a step by step list of How to Read to a Small Child as well. This list may be as short or as long as the group chooses, but should include: Hold the child, read slowly and clearly, stop to ask for questions, show the pictures the child, relate the story line to the child's life, and ask the child questions about the story, calling this question period a "game" to see what the child remembers from the story.

 **HOW TO PLAY**

Play of the Game
Students are given the handouts at the start of the activity. Discussion should include adding or deleting from the Read to Me list as they choose. The educator should then make a step by step list for "How to Read to a Small Child" with the help of the group. They may then each choose a

children's book, and take turns reading aloud.   The other members of the group should give constructive suggestions after each reader.

 **Teacher Tips**

The possibility that the parents may never have been read to themselves is, unfortunately, very real. Be sensitive as well to low lever learners among the group, and be careful to avoid an uncomfortable situation.   Allowing volunteers as readers, honoring "I pass", and encouraging one on one communication with the group members should ease over a potentially embarrassing moment.   Above all, reinforce that parenting is learned one day at a time, and that we're all learning.   Encourage reading to little ones who can't provide feedback as well.   Setting a pattern where children are held, cuddled, touched and read to provides many opportunities for tactile enjoyment for both parent and child.   At the onset of the "readings," teens in particular may express dismay at the "corniess" of the exercise.   Inevitably, however, this activity is very enjoyable to all involved.

Helping Parents Create New Readers is a Gift for ALL our Futures.

Knowledge is Power!!

Good for You Card Game

Subject: Encourages positive self awareness and reinforcement of good parenting skills
Target Population: New parents, especially young men and women
Suitable For: Males, females or co-ed groups
Props Needed: Cards, as below

Time: Approximately 15 minutes

OVERVIEW
The Good for You Card Game reinforces good parenting while encouraging positive self awareness among new parents. Young parents in particular can benefit from positive feedback on their parenting skills.

BEHAVIORAL OBJECTIVES
At the end of the game, the participants will:
♦ State three good parenting skills they possess
♦ Discuss parenting as an on-going calling with challenging choices on a daily basis

---

PREPARATION - "Setting the Stage"
Prior to the session, the educator should prepare several sets of cards (one per parent in the class) that list positive parenting skills. Each card is worth a pre-determined number of points. For example - *Hugged your toddler for no reason* may be worth 4 points.

Examples of these skills on the cards may be:

* Hugged your toddler for no reason
* Used "I" messages with your toddler or young child
* Read to your baby
* Played a game with your child
* Sang songs with your little one

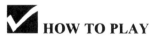 **HOW TO PLAY**

Play of the Game
Students are given a set of cards at the start of the game. Going around the group, each parent "plays" a card by placing it in the middle of the table. He or she then relays the incident with their child when the parenting occurred. Members of the group may comment or challenge at any time. The parent then tallies their points. Highest score wins.

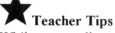 **Teacher Tips**

While an excellent opportunity to reinforce good parenting, be sensitive to parents who are just beginning to develop awareness into parenting as a skill. Model positive reinforcement within the group, using phrases such as "I can see how hard you're working at being a good parent." Reframe parental comments about their children, for example "He's so bad" in reference to a toddler by saying. "He's busy at this stage, isn't he?" Explain that "bad" can be a self-fulfilling label to a child.

Make a Reader Game

Subject: Encourage literacy

Target Population: New parents, especially young men and women

Suitable For: Males, females or co-ed groups

Props Needed: Photo albums
                  Scissors
                  Glue
                  Magazines

Time: Approximately 40 minutes

OVERVIEW

The Make a Reader Game reinforces reading as an important way to connect with a young child while tailoring the reading experience to the needs of the individual children.

BEHAVIORAL OBJECTIVES

At the end of the game, the participants will be able to:

♦ Create a "book" to read to their young child

PREPARATION - "Setting the Stage"

Prior to the session, the educator should prepare sample readers.

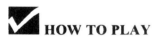 **HOW TO PLAY**

Play of the Game

Students are given supplies and asked to create a "book" for their child or children. Each page of the book should contain one picture and words or phrases that identify the picture. For example, a child who loves dogs would have pictures of dogs in the book, with phrases beneath the pictures describing the dog and the dog's activity.

 **Teacher Tips**

The books should be highly personal - the cover should read "_____ (Child's Name's) Book"- and should contain pictures of interest to that individual child. This gives the educator an opportunity to oversee parent child bonding as comments are made about the child and the child's interests.

Child Safety Bingo Game

Subject: Childproof and safe environments
Target Population: New parents, especially young men and women
Suitable For: Males, females or co-ed groups
Props Needed: Bingo cards (as below)

Time: Approximately 20 minutes

OVERVIEW
Safety Bingo presents childproof and safe environments within the confines of a common game, bingo.

BEHAVIORAL OBJECTIVES
At the end of the game, the participants will be able to:
♦ Describe a safe environment for a small child or infant

PREPARATION - "Setting the Stage"
Prior to the session, the educator should prepare bingo cards. Each square should contain an example of a healthy or safe environment choice. The word CHILD should be used instead of the word bingo at the top of the cards. Cards should also be prepared corresponding to those choices to allow for "calling."
Possible squares may include:
* A smoke free environment
* Locks on doors
* Car seats and seatbelts
* Examples of age appropriate foods

 HOW TO PLAY
Play of the Game
The game runs just like bingo, with normal bingo rules and regulations. Students can add or delete items at will.

 Teacher Tips
Modeling appropriate child care must always be discrete. Be sensitive to parents who haven't complied with safety regulations, and encourage that behavior.

Make a Baby Book

Subject: Reinforcement of good parenting skills and awareness of normal growth and development
Target Population: New parents, especially young men and women
Suitable For: Males, females or co-ed groups
Props Needed: Small photo albums or scrapbooks
      Pictures
      Scissors
      Glue
      Ribbon, lace and stickers for decoration
          Time: Approximately 20 minutes

OVERVIEW

Make a Baby Book, while not exactly a game, provides an opportunity for an educator to develop rapport, conduct an informal discussion on parenting, and reinforce good parenting while the activity is in process.

BEHAVIORAL OBJECTIVES

At the end of the game, the participants will be able to:

◆ Name their child's current developmental stage
◆ Discuss parenting as an on-going calling with challenging choices on a daily basis

---

PREPARATION - "Setting the Stage"

Prior to the session, the educator should create several sample small baby books using the supplies listed above. This book may depict any children as subjects, but must reflect diversity and cross cultural awareness.

 **HOW TO PLAY**

Play of the Game

Students are given the supplies and asked to create a baby book for their child, reflecting the child's current stage of development.

Educator Tips

Discussion that occurs during this relaxing activity can be important to an educator's better understanding of the parent's point of view. Be especially vigilant to young teens who have difficulty relating to the concept of a baby book. It may be helpful to bring in actual baby books of the educator's children or that of a friend's children. Parenting is a learned art. It is very possible that some young parents have little to no frame of reference for positive parenting, since their own childhood experience was truncated. In situations like those, the educator can often be placed in the role of surrogate parent for the teen parent him or herself.

Building "Block" Nutrition Bingo Game

Subject: Good nutrition for children
Target Population: New parents, especially young men and women
Suitable For: Males, females or co-ed groups
Props Needed: Bingo cards (as below)
Cookbooks
Cards (as below)

Time: Approximately 40 minutes

OVERVIEW
Nutrition Bingo presents good nutrition within the confines of a non-traditional bingo game.

BEHAVIORAL OBJECTIVES
At the end of the game, the participants will be able to:
♦ Design a healthy diet for a small child or infant

PREPARATION - "Setting the Stage"
Prior to the session, the educator should prepare bingo cards. Each square in the cards should be blank. The word BLOCK should be used instead of the word bingo at the top of the cards. Cards should also be prepared with the nutritional building blocks in the following categories:
Protein, Carbohydrate, Vitamin, Calcium, Fat, etc.

 HOW TO PLAY

Play of the Game
Parents begin with a blank card and write an item from their child's diet (using a representative 24 hour period) in each square of the card. The educator draws from the nutrition building block cards and reads each aloud. The students mark off any square that corresponds to a nutritional building block that was served to their child during the day chosen.

Educator Tips
As always, modeling appropriate child care must always involve care. Be sensitive to parents who haven't provided good nutrition for their child, and encourage more positive behavior

Chapter Seven
Games for Breastfeeding Education

She is their earth......
she is their food and their bed
and the extra blanket when it
grows cold in the night.....

....Katherine Butler Hathaway

Breastfeeding Postpartum Role Play #1: Mom's Mom

Subject: Breastfeeding and postpartum adjustment
Target Population: Potential breastfeeding or currently nursing mothers
Suitable For: Males, females or co-ed groups.
            See Adolescent Special Needs Section to adapt for teens
Props Needed:
        Baby doll
        Bottle
        Apron
        Hat
        Blanket
        Flip chart
        Cards (as below)

                                Time: Approximately 10 - 15 minutes

OVERVIEW

The Breastfeeding Postpartum Role Play addresses the reality of breastfeeding as it impacts upon a new mothers. Varied scenarios can be created to enhance the experience of a father, grandmother, sibling, etc.

BEHAVIORAL OBJECTIVES

At the end of the game, the participants will be able to:

♦ Role play or participant as an observer in one of the scenarios
♦ List three areas where support is vital for a new breastfeeding mother
♦ Discuss the role of a partner or supportive relative in a successful breastfeeding experience

---
PREPARATION - "Setting the Stage"
Role play is a potentially threatening exercise for some segments of the population (see Section of manual on role play). Give participants permission to "pass" and not play.

Make small cards (3 X 5 works well) that assign roles as follows:
New Mom, New Dad, Grandma A (mother of the new Mom)

Make cards that list the role scenarios below:
Mom Scenario: You are a new mother with a five week old nursing infant. Your baby is fussy, and keeps you awake most nights for long periods. Your mother is visiting from out of state. She didn't nurse any of her children.

Dad Scenario: You are a new father with a five week old infant. Your wife is nursing. You are supportive of her breastfeeding, but right now you're exhausted from getting up nights and would be thrilled if ANYONE could show you how to make your baby sleep for longer periods.

Grandma A Scenario: You are a first time grandmother. You had three children - this is your youngest child and only daughter. You bottle fed all your children
---

 **HOW TO PLAY**

Play of the Game

- Assign roles. For extra fun, let participants "gender switch" (an actual expectant mom could portray the expectant father). This can open many discussions. With reluctant participants, or to start things off, assume a role yourself

- Initiate discussion by passing out the scenarios.

- Keep discussion going throughout the role play by making comments, such as:
    - ⇒ What do you say if Grandma blames the baby's fussiness on breastfeeding?
    - ⇒ How does the father respond in that case?

- Ask couples in the room to brainstorm (use a wipe off board or flip chart) potential problems and areas where support is needed

 **Educator Tips**

Assuming the role of grandma will enable the real parents to react to a theoretical situation that may be only too real. The drama provides a safe environment for open discussion. Be careful to set a positive overall tone, and underscore the very real possibility that "Grandma" may be the most supportive of all. Any other friend or relative who may, with the best of intentions, sabotage a positive nursing relationship, may be substituted for the "Grandma" role.

Limit the time to allow for discussion from the "non-acting" portion of the class

Adolescent Special Needs

The challenges of intergenerational living compound normal adjustments in many adolescent's homes. the stark reality of facing conflict between the teen and her mother. Be aware and sensitive to the following points:

- Sharing a baby is never easy, under the best of conditions. Teen parents need to identify themselves as the parent of the baby, and may have genuine concerns as to "who" is in charge. This may compound the sharing problems.

- Many people frown on the idea of teens breastfeeding. Preparing adolescent mothers for breastfeeding by stressing the strengthening of the mother infant bond may give them the confidence they need to at least initiate the nursing experience.

- The reality of shared living space in a three generation environment may be harsh. The babies' grandparents may feel left out while the young parent feels threatened. Opening discussion in this volatile area often requires someone from outside of the family.

- Feelings of guilt or regret associated with early childbearing on the part of grandparents may manifest itself in resistance to breastfeeding. This is particularly true when there has been no successful breastfeeding model in the family.

Breastfeeding Role Play #2 - Dad's Mom

Subject: Breastfeeding and postpartum adjustment
Target Population: Potential breastfeeding or currently nursing mother
Suitable For: Males, females or co-ed groups.
Props Needed:
      Baby doll
      Bottle
      Blanket
      Breast model
      Breast pump
      Cards (as below)

Time: Approximately 10 - 15 minutes

OVERVIEW
The Breastfeeding Postpartum Role Play #2 addresses the reality of breastfeeding as it impacts upon a new mothers. This variation switches roles for the grandparents.

BEHAVIORAL OBJECTIVES
At the end of the game, the participants will be able to:
♦ Role play or participant as an observer in one of the scenarios
♦ List three areas where support is vital for a new breastfeeding mother
♦ Discuss the role of a partner or supportive relative in a successful breastfeeding experience

---

PREPARATION - "Setting the Stage"
Make small cards (3 X 5 works well) that assign roles as follows:
New Mom, New Dad, Grandma B (mother of the new Dad)

Make cards that list the scenarios below:
Mom Scenario: You are a new mother, with a five week old nursing infant. Your baby is fussy, and keeps you awake most nights for long periods. Your mother in law is visiting from out of state. She didn't nurse any of her children.

Dad Scenario: You are a new father, with a five week old infant. Your wife is nursing. You are supportive of her breastfeeding, but right now you're exhausted from getting up nights and would be thrilled if ANYONE could show you how to make your baby sleep for longer periods.

Grandma B Scenario: You are a first time grandmother. This (the new Dad) is your only child. You bottle fed him.

 **HOW TO PLAY**

Play of the Game

As with Breastfeeding Role Play #1, with the revised dynamics inherent in the role of father's mom as the "invading" grandma. Comments should encourage positive communication between expectant parents in the class, and ideally should stimulate discussion of the role of the father in the breastfeeding dyad.

 **Educator Tips**

Assuming the role of grandma will enable the real parents to react to a theoretical situation that may be only too real. The drama provides a safe environment for open discussion. Be careful to set a positive overall tone, and underscore the very real possibility that "Grandma" may be the most supportive of all. Any other friend or relative who may, with the best of intentions, sabotage a positive nursing relationship, may be substituted for the "Grandma" role.

Limit the time to allow for discussion from the "non-acting" portion of the class

Breastfeeding Role Play - Teens at School

Subject: Breastfeeding and postpartum adjustment for adolescents returning to   school
Target Population: Potential breastfeeding or currently nursing mother
Suitable For: Males, females or co-ed groups.
Props Needed: Cards (as below)

Time: Approximately 10 - 15 minutes

OVERVIEW
The Breastfeeding Role Play - Teens at School addresses the reality of breastfeeding as it impacts upon returning to school. Potential conflicts with faculty or students are discussed and possible solutions brainstormed.

BEHAVIORAL OBJECTIVES
At the end of the game, the participants will be able to:
♦   Role play or participant as an observer in one of the scenarios
♦   List two areas of potential conflict when attempting to maintain a breastfeeding relationship and returning to school
♦   Discuss possible solutions or areas of support for the breastfeeding teen

---

PREPARATION - "Setting the Stage"
Prior to the role play, the educator should prepare scenarios cards to reflect possible areas of conflict within the school system. Some areas of concern may be:

You are a new breastfeeding mom returning to your high school after giving birth. You need to pump between 10:00 - 11:00 AM, but your instructor at that time frame won't give you a pass to the nurses office. You are told that you can pump "between classes" (there is a four minute time limit in between classes at your school.) How do you handle this situation?

Your friends think that your baby is great, but they can't believe you've decide to nurse. "You're going to let a baby suck on you! That's too gross" one of them says. How do you respond?

Your favorite teacher appears to be supportive of your pregnancy and birth. When she finds out that you're nursing, she says: "You're doing what? It'll ruin your body? You're too young to nurse a baby!" What can you say to her that is respectful yet shows how you really feel?

It's past time for you to pump, but your teacher won't let you leave. When you finally reach the nurse's office, ready to "explode", there are so many other students there you can't find a place to pump in private. You loose your temper and storm out of the office. The principal sees you angry and gives you after school detention, making it impossible for you to pick up your baby at day care. To whom do you turn for help?

 **HOW TO PLAY**

Play of the Game

Students choose a card and read the scenario. The group responds in an informal fashion. Remember to ask the group where teens can go for assistance in situations like these in local high schools. You may want to write down the names of supportive faculty or guidance personnel, and pass it on to subsequent parenting teens from the same school district.

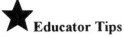 **Educator Tips**

Remember a breastfeeding teen often needs to be assertive. Model assertive, not aggressive behavior, however. (These scenarios are all based on actual experiences teens in our Outreach have encountered)

Breastfeeding Lunch Box

Subject: Breastfeeding benefits

Target Population: Potential breastfeeding parents or currently nursing mothers

Suitable For: Males, females or co-ed groups.

Props Needed: Lunch box

Dollar bill	*Match box car*
Thermometer	*Small round rubber ball*
Tape measure	*Newborn diaper*
Small clock	*Small diploma*
Retainer	*Small children's book*
Heart	

Time: Approximately 10 - 15 minutes

OVERVIEW

The Breastfeednig Lunch Box reinforces breastfeeding as a positive choice

BEHAVIORAL OBJECTIVES

At the end of the game, the participants will be able to:

♦ List three benefits of breastfeeding to babies

♦ List three benefits of breastfeeding to moms

PREPARATION

Prior to the session, the educator should fill the lunch box with the items listed.

Each of them represent a benefit for breastfeeding as follows:

Dollar bill = Cost savings

Match box car = Portable baby

Thermometer = Fewer infections - + immunity

Small round ball = Size of baby's stomach = baby knows when he or she is full

Tape measure = Return of mom to pre-pregnancy weight faster

Newborn diaper = Less odor in diapers

Small clock = Saves time

Small diploma = Increases intelligence

Retainer = Good jaw development

Small children's book = Can read to a toddler while nursing

Heart = Wonderful maternal infant bonding

 HOW TO PLAY

Play of the Game

Students choose an item from the lunch box in turn and discuss the relationship of that item to breastfeeding benefits

 Teacher Tips

Encourage additions to the "lunch box" as students discover benefits of their own.

© 1996 *Games Educators Play*

"Birth Parent" for this game = Teresa Shilling, MS, FACCE

Chapter Eight Games for Professional Workshops

*Real Education should
educate us out of self into
something far finer;
into a selflessness
which links us to all
humanity*

....Lady Nancy Astor

What's In a Name?

Subject: Increased awareness of birth as normal
Target Population: Adults working with birthing women
Suitable For: Males, females or co-ed groups
Props Needed: List words associated with birth (see below)

Time: Approximately 10 minutes

OVERVIEW

What's in a Name? Focuses upon the terminology used to describe birth. Reframing the birth culture requires an awareness of birth as normal for professionals as well birthing women and their partners.

BEHAVIORAL OBJECTIVES

At the end of the game, the participants will be able to:

♦ Define birth as normal
♦ Re-phrase terminology associated with birth to reflect normalcy instead of illness

---

PREPARATION - "Setting the Stage"

Prior to the session, the educator should develop a list of medical terms commonly used in birth and birthing situations, as well as more "normal" terms that could replace them. An example of that list would include:

Common Term:	*Reframe and Embrace:*
Fetus	Baby
Labor	The Birth Process
Delivery	Birth
Delivery Suite or LDR	Birthing Suite or LBR
Coping (as in labor, birth)	Managing (as in labor, birth)
Labor Pain	Labor Work
Birth Plan	Birth Guidelines
Cesarean Section	Cesarean Birth
Adequate Pelvis	Capable Pelvis
Failure to Progress	Pause in Labor
Expected Date of Confinement	Approximate Birth Date
Girls, Ladies	Women
Control during Labor	(Avoid) Remember that Birth is Uncontrollable
Give up for Adoption	Choose to Place the Baby with Another Family
Losing a Baby	The Baby Died

"Birth Parent" for this game = Mary Jo Podgurski, RNC, MA, FACCE

 **HOW TO PLAY**

Play of the Game

The game may be conducted as a match game, or with the discussion leader dividing the participants into small groups and providing them with a handout that addressees each of the above issues in a question. For example, the handout may ask: Give me the word used to describe the room where the baby is usually born. (Birthing Suite not Delivery Suite)

**Educator Tips**

Seeking to reframe a person's perception of long standing cultural terms is not easy. Model a non-judgmental acceptance of the participants and encourage open discussion. Even one person with an altered mindset is a victory!

Place a Human Face on the Numbers Game

Subject: Stereotypes of pregnant teens
Target Population: Professional adults
Suitable For: Males, females or co-ed groups
Props Needed: Handout of drawing paper
　　　　　　　　Pencil
　　　　　　　　Markers or crayons
　　　　　　　　Chalkboard, flip chart or wipe off board

Time: Approximately 10 minutes

OVERVIEW
The Place a Human Face on the Numbers Game seeks to dispel stereotypes that surround images of pregnant and parenting teens.

BEHAVIORAL OBJECTIVES
At the end of the game, the participants will be able to:
♦ Draw a pre-session picture of a pregnant or parenting teen
♦ List typical stereotypes of pregnant and parenting teens
♦ Draw a post-session picture of a pregnant or parenting teen
♦ Assess differences in pre and post impressions (if any)

PREPARATION - "Setting the Stage"
Prior to the session, the educator should prepare handouts with a vague shape of a female form on it. Two handouts will be needed per participant.

 HOW TO PLAY

Play of the Game
The educator asks the participants to draw their perception of a pregnant or parenting teen. Those who choose to draw a "word picture" may do so. The pictures should be set aside while group discussion lists typical stereotypes of pregnant and parenting teens and then dispels them with statistics when possible. Participants should then be given a clean sheet of paper and asked to revise their image, if they choose to do so.

 Educator Tips
Remember that not everyone considers themselves an artist and allow participants to use words to describe their images. If the discussion doesn't inspire the removal of at least some of the stereotypes associated with these young women, direct discussion to the origins of the groups perception.

Can You See Me? Game

Subject: Denial of HIV/AIDS risk
Target Population: Professional adults
Suitable For: Males, females or co-ed groups
Props Needed: Handout of drawing paper
               Pencil
               Markers or crayons
               Chalkboard, flip chart or wipe off board

Time: Approximately 15 minutes

OVERVIEW
The Can You See Me? Game seeks to remove denial of HIV/AIDS as a significant health care problem. Even professionals may see the HIV infected individual as belonging to "other" groups, and subsequently invisible.

BEHAVIORAL OBJECTIVES
At the end of the game, the participants will be able to:
- Draw a pre-session picture of a HIV positive individual
- List typical stereotypes of a HIV positive individual
- Draw a post-session picture of a HIV positive individual
- Assess differences in pre and post impressions (if any)

PREPARATION - "Setting the Stage"
Prior to the session, the educator should prepare handouts with a vague shape of a human form on it. Two handouts will be needed per participant.
Obtain current information on local, national and international rates of HIV/AIDS infection, focusing on rates for adolescents and women.

 HOW TO PLAY

Play of the Game
The educator asks the participants to draw their perception of a HIV infected individual Those who choose to draw a "word picture" may do so. The pictures should be set aside while group discussion lists typical stereotypes of HIV/AIDS infection and then dispels them with statistics when possible. Participants should then be given a clean sheet of paper and asked to revise their image, if they choose to do so.

 Educator Tips
Remember that not everyone considers themselves an artist and allow participants to use words to describe their images. If the discussion doesn't inspire the removal of at least some of the stereotypes associated HIV/AIDS infection, direct discussion to the origins of the groups perception.

Risk Takers Game

Subject: Empathic identification with others, especially adults with teens
Target Population: Works best with adults
Suitable For: Males, females or co-ed groups
Props Needed: List of risks

Time: Approximately 10 minutes

OVERVIEW

The Risk Takers Game is a quick game that superficially appears to be light hearted, but can spark serious thinking, especially with an adult group in a workshop or training situation.

BEHAVIORAL OBJECTIVES

At the end of the game, the participants will be able to:

♦ Access themselves for risk taking behaviors
♦ Acknowledge risk- taking as a behavioral script for adolescents
♦ Connect adolescent risk taking with adult risk taking.

PREPARATION - "Setting the Stage"
Prior to the session, the educator should develop a list of risks. The risks should begin with common experiences and become more complex. Early risks mentioned may include: Driving without a seat belt, Driving above the speed limit, Consuming red meat, Cutting a class, Eating high fat foods, Smoking, Drinking one alcoholic drink, Jaywalking, Parking in a no parking zone. Moderate risks may include: Smoking a marijuana cigarette, Cheating on income taxes, Leaving the door unlocked at night (dependent upon location!), Walking alone at night in a strange city, Becoming intoxicated, Driving after consuming alcohol. Be cautious with serious risks that may engender guilt or difficult memories. Tailor the risks to the group. **Give participants the right to "Pass."**

 HOW TO PLAY

Play of the Game
The educator asks the group to evaluate their personal risk taking quotient by giving themselves three points for each of the risks mentioned.   Participants tally their own scores, which are kept confidential. At the end of the game, the educator asks if anyone has accumulated more than 10 points. Brief discussion can evolve to - ARE ADULTS RISK TAKERS? . HOW ARE WE DIFFERENT FROM TEENS?

 Educator Tips

A few introductory words will "set the stage" and make participants more aware of your objectives. An example of an introduction is to simply state: "Before we judge others, particularly teens who take risks, let's examine ourselves to see if we're risk takers." The educator's attitude is important: the tone of the words used to introduce this game should be inclusive - the educator is presenting him or herself as a risk taker as well - and non-judgmental

Creative Teaching Strategies

Subject: Creative teaching
Target Population: Childbirth educators
Suitable For: Males, females or co-ed groups
Props Needed: Scenario cards (see below)

Time: Approximately 20 minutes

OVERVIEW
Creative Teaching Techniques is an excellent way to involve professionals in active teaching..

BEHAVIORAL OBJECTIVES
At the end of the game, the participants will be able to:
♦ Role play creative teaching techniques in varied situations

---

PREPARATION - "Setting the Stage"
Prior to the session, the educator should prepare cards with potential scenarios for creative teaching. Such scenarios should be fun, educational, and easy to role play. Examples of such scenarios are:

You are the only educator in an in-school clinic. A fifteen year old student approaches you and tells you that her due date is only a month away. To add to this confusing information, she tells you that she's transferring to another school tomorrow! What can you teach her about labor and birth in a short time, using only your body and a chalkboard as visual aids?

One of your clients in childbirth class is legally blind. Create a teaching strategy that would help her visualize labor and birth.

Your childbirth education class is made up of an extremely diverse group of people. On one end of the career spectrum is a artist, at the other end, an attorney. You are also teaching a very young mother - fourteen - and a first time mother who is forty-four. What creative teaching strategy could you develop that would appeal to all these mothers?

 HOW TO PLAY
Play of the Game
This game is a basic role play and should follow rules as such. Small groups work best, with reporting done to the whole workshop at the end of the program.

Educator Tips
The many and diverse reactions you will receive to this game make it well worth while. A good learning experience for the educator and participants.

Families!!

Subject: Dysfunctional family groups
Target Population: Adult professionals
Suitable For: Males, females or co-ed groups
Props Needed: Scenario cards (see below)
Identity cards (see below)

Time: Approximately 20 minutes

OVERVIEW
Families!! explores the dynamics of functional and dysfunctional families in a role play situation that is conducive to open discussion.

BEHAVIORAL OBJECTIVES
At the end of the game, the participants will be able to:
♦   Role play reactions of different family members to common life scenarios

---

PREPARATION - "Setting the Stage"
Prior to the session, the educator should prepare cards with potential scenarios, as well as identification labels or cards. For example, the identification labels could list the roles of: Hero, Scapegoat, Lost Child.

Some common scenarios may be:
*   You return home from school to find your mother passed out drunk on the living room floor. What do you do?
*   Your grandfather dies. How do you react?
*   You (or your girlfriend) discover a pregnancy has begun. Neither of you are ready to be parents. How do handle this news?
*   You think your best friend is HIV positive. Do you tell anyone?

 ## HOW TO PLAY
Play of the Game
The participants should be divided into small groups and assigned a "family" role. Scenarios should be given to each family. A discussion leader is chosen in each group. Each member of the "family" gives their probable reaction to the scenarios in turn.

Educator Tips
Be sure to model avoidance of stereotypes. Atypical behavior is the hallmark of humankind. Remember that the reactions you are role playing may vary from individual to individual. Follow up the role play by discussing the role of a professional (educator, counselor, etc) to these varied situations.

Preparing Women to be Assertive in Labor/Birth

Subject: Empathic identification with others, especially adults with teens
Target Population: Childbirth educators
Suitable For: Males, females or co-ed groups
Props Needed: Cards (as below)
Handout (as below)

Time: Approximately 20 minutes

OVERVIEW
Preparing Women to be Assertive in Labor/Birth addresses an important area of childbirth education that is often overlooked. Assertive, not aggressive, responses are vital in some birthing situations.

BEHAVIORAL OBJECTIVES
At the end of the game, the participants will be able to:
♦ Differentiate among passive, assertive, and aggressive responses
♦ Role play an assertive response to a labor or birth related scenario

---

PREPARATION - "Setting the Stage"
Prior to the session, the educator should develop a handout of examples of passive, assertive, and aggressive responses. Examples of each are:
Passive: You're the doctor. Whatever you think is best for me is OK.
Assertive: I'd like to know the pros and cons of the procedure you're ordering for me.
Aggressive: I've been watching Hard Copy, and I know that you doctors only want money from me. I'm watching you!

Scenario cards should be developed for role play. Some should be silly, some serious. An example of a serious situation is:
You are a woman pregnant with your first baby. For the last several months, your caregiver and your family have consistently said "Wow, big baby" when they look at you. Now, you're due in a few days, and nothing's happening. Your caregiver recommends induction due to the size of the baby. Your cervix is not effaced or dilated. In spite of your anxiety about your baby's size, you would prefer to allow labor to begin on its own.

 HOW TO PLAY
Play of the Game
After general discussion regarding types of responses, students should choose a card and react in three ways to the scenario: With a passive, assertive, or aggressive response.

 Educator Tips
Be careful to avoid "inducing" anxiety or preparing your clients to be angry. Model assertive responses in class on an on-going basis. Discussion can evolve into decision making and refusal skills as well.

Where Do You Stand!?

Subject: Belief systems
Target Population: Sexuality educators
Suitable For: Males, females or co-ed groups
Props Needed: List of questions

Time: Approximately 15 minutes

OVERVIEW
Where Do You Stand!? addresses some of the controversial issues surrounding sexuality education.

BEHAVIORAL OBJECTIVES
At the end of the game, the participants will be able to:

♦ Assess their personal position on controversial issues

PREPARATION - "Setting the Stage"
Prior to the session, a list of questions touching on controversial issues within sexuality education should be compiled. Such questions may include:

What is abstinence?
How far should a teen "go" sexually?
How old should a teen be before they have sex?
Should all teens wait for marriage to have sex?

 HOW TO PLAY
Play of the Game
The educator should address the group and present the questions one at a time. Small groups should be formed to allow for discussion. After the small group discussion, the leader should set an imaginary line, or continuum, in the front of the room. Allowing for "I Pass", the leader will then invite participants to join him/her on the continuum, professing their beliefs by standing in the place on the continuum that best represents what they "stand" for. For example, one end of the continuum for the questions "How far should a teen "go" sexually?" may be "Nothing at all" or "Holding hands" while the other end of the continuum may be "Anything but vaginal penetration."

 Educator Tips
Model a non-judgmental attitude. These topics are volatile and involve deep emotions. A frank discussion in these areas can be extremely productive and may even lead to a compromise among caring educators at opposite ends of the spectrum

Chapter Nine
Games for
All
Groups

*Education should convert
the mind into a living
fountain...
not a reservoir*

... John M. Mason

Stand Up, Sit Down Game

Subject: Icebreaker, encourages respect for individual differences
Target Population: Easily adaptable to any group. Works best with middle school students, although may be successfully used in an adult seminar or workshop
Suitable For: Males, females or co-ed groups
Props Needed: List of questions

Time: Approximately 10 minutes

OVERVIEW
Stand up, sit down is an easy game to play as a first game or icebreaker. It can be adapted to serve any audience, and questions can be incorporated to render the game more serious if the educator so chooses.

BEHAVIORAL OBJECTIVES
At the end of the game, the participants will be able to:
♦ Acknowledge the informality of the presentation ahead
♦ Assess other participants and self for positive differences
♦ Discuss acceptance of the differences of others

PREPARATION - "Setting the Stage"
Prior to the session, the educator should develop a list of questions to be asked during the play of the game Sample questions for all ages may be: Stand up if you have one sister, two sisters, etc. Stand up if you have one dog, two dogs, etc. Sample questions for middle school students may be: Stand up if you play basketball, the flute, etc. Sample questions for adults in a workshop may be: Stand up if you work with pregnant teens, parenting teens, in a school, in a clinic, etc. Examples of serious questions are: For students - Stand up if you know anyone who smokes cigarettes, has smoked weed, etc. **Be very careful when asking personal or serious questions.** With adults, serious questions may include: Stand up if you've taught abstinence only sexuality education in the past, stand up if you've taught comprehensive sexuality education in the past, etc. **Avoid standing for belief systems, and give participants the right to "Pass."**

 **HOW TO PLAY**

Play of the Game
The educator asks several questions (see preparation) of the group in rapid succession.
Participants stand when the question asked applies to them, and then return quickly to their seats

 Educator Tips
Explain that no one is forced to participant, and explain the "I Pass" concept. A "trial run" works extremely well - for example, simply running through a quick, easy question makes the group understand the concept of play. Participants should be told to sit down quickly after they stand in answer to a question that applies to them, since the next question will follow in a few seconds.

Group Selection #1

Subject: Dividing into small groups for discussion
Target Population: Easily adaptable to any group.
Suitable For: Males, females or co-ed groups
Props Needed: Select one set per game:
> Varied colored poker chips
> Assorted individually wrapped candy
> Assorted brands of gum
> Varied colored Post-it type paper
> Assorted colors of stamp pads
> Assorted colors - washable markers
> Pre-marked folders of handouts
> Pre-numbered cards

Time: Approximately 5 minutes

OVERVIEW
Group Selection #1 is more a group process activity than a game. It allows for ease in selection of small groups while providing diversity in group composition.

BEHAVIORAL OBJECTIVES
At the end of the game, the participants will be able to:
- Align themselves into groups as per selection
- Discuss the initial stages of group process

PREPARATION - "Setting the Stage"
Prior to the session, the educator should choose the type of selection best for this group. A simple basket can contain the poker chips, gum, candy, etc. Members of the class or workshop choose a color or type of gum, candy, etc. Pre-numbered cards or marks on folders and handouts must be prepared before class begins. Class members are grouped according to their selections.

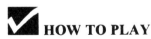 HOW TO PLAY

Play of the Game
This process will only take a few moments of your class time, but will allow for easy flow as groups form.

 Educator Tips

Encourage friends, professionals from the same agency, or homogeneous groups to divide and form heterogeneous groups for discussion. The first time selection of this type occurs in a school, students are usually quite compliant, but will try to manipulate selection once they understand why they are choosing candy, chips, etc. In that case, simply having students enter the room and count off every third or fourth person will work well..

Group Selection #2

Subject: Self-selection into small groups for discussion
Target Population: Easily adaptable to any group.
Suitable For: Males, females or co-ed groups
Props Needed: Paper, markers, tape or clips

Time: Approximately 5 minutes

OVERVIEW
Group Selection #2 allows self selection of small groups to encourage a heterogeneous group composition.

BEHAVIORAL OBJECTIVES
At the end of the game, the participants will be able to:
- ♦ Align themselves into groups as per selection
- ♦ Discuss the initial stages of group process

PREPARATION - "Setting the Stage"

Prior to the session, the educator should choose the type of self selection best for this group.
Small posters can be made to describe the groups composition. The posters can then be distributed around the class or meeting room, taped to walls or clipped onto flip charts.
Sample self selection topics may include:
Birthday Month
Favorite Color
Sun Sign
Association with certain words - for example: "Giving Birth, Being Delivered" for childbirth educators
Association with controversial areas - for example: "Abstinence Education, Abstinence Based Education, Comprehensive Education" for sexuality educators

---

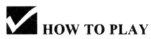 **HOW TO PLAY**

Play of the Game
This process will only take a few moments of your class time, but will allow for easy flow as groups form.

 Educator Tips

In some groups, self selection simply doesn't provide a heterogeneous group. In those cases, Group Selection #1 will be more effective.

Chapter Ten
Role Play

*Imagination is
the highest kite
we can fly*

.... Lauren Bacall

Role Play

Overview

Perhaps there is no learning technique that is more fraught with potential anxiety than *role play*, or impromptu dramatics. Yet, I believe there are few tools that can more completely allow the student to apply what is being taught. Research has demonstrated that human beings most easily retain the things they actively do, as opposed to that which is given to them in a passive modality. (Fuhrman and Grasha, 1983; McKeachie, 1986) For example a youth approaching a driver's test for the first time is far more likely to pass if he or she has had the benefit of a supervised driver's education course that involved actual hands on driving. If driver's education relied only upon reading about parallel parking I am certain the student would not be adequately prepared. Educators realize, however, that it often not practical, or even possible, to provide similar walk-through for some experiences. In childbirth education, the well-known practice of simulating a contraction or holding a labor rehearsal attempt to make "real" skills learned in class. A well-directed role play can be adjusted to almost any teaching arena, and can provide for a feasible and realistic learning experience.

Description

In a role-playing game or activity, the students are given a realistic or hypothetical situation and a cast of characters. Scenarios may be changed during the game. The students then improvise dramatic dialogue and actions to fit their characters and their perception of the scenarios. In a childbirth class, for example, an expectant mother may be given the scenario that she feels a strong urge to push and is told not to bear down by her caregivers. Others in the class may be assigned the roles of nurse, midwife, obstetrician, support person, etc.

Role Play Hints

⇒ **Never force - always give permission for "I Pass" (non-participation)**
⇒ **Introduce the role play *after* a sense of trust is established with the group and yourself whenever possible**
⇒ **Model the behavior you wish your students to exhibit.** For example, initiate the role play by "performing" yourself if possible, and permitting the students a chance to observe
⇒ **Approach the role play with a relaxed, matter of fact attitude**
⇒ **Hold fast to your sense of humor**
⇒ **Avoid scripted role plays - they "put words in your mouth" and stifle creativity and free expression**
⇒ **Allow students to craft their own role play, using a few simple props (phones are great)!**
⇒ **Direct non-judgmental comments and discussion by example**
⇒ **Set guidelines prior to starting the role play (see Setting the Stage for Role Play)**

Setting the Stage for Role Play

Suggest role play to an audience of students -- especially adult learners -- and you will more than likely hear a chorus of groans. Adults in particular may remember uncomfortable strained moments when they were forced to participate in a similar kind of event in their past. To ease your students' minds, I recommend the following:

- *Model A Relaxed Approach to Decrease Participant Anxiety:* The educator sets the tone for the role play. Model a relaxed approach - practice in front of a mirror if you need to - and look as if you're genuinely having fun. (I hope you are) Acknowledge potential anxiety with a sense of humor, not by denying it exists. (The elephant in the living room!)

- *Set Guidelines:* The old adage that one should begin as one wishes to end is certainly true in a role playing situation. Important rules regarding discriminatory or biased comments should idealistically be part of your normal contact with a class, and will only need reinforcement here. When the post-role play discussion occurs, it is important that those who participated in the role play be free from ridicule.

- *Be Informal:* Ideally the role play could be run simultaneously by all members of the class. This would remove the feeling of being on "center stage" that is a turn-off to so many people who fear role playing. Divide the class into small groups and let every one play out the same scenarios. After students are more comfortable with role play, some students may act only as observers.

- *Choose Meaningful Scenarios:* Nothing is more frustrating than a class that is only "going through the motions" to please the teacher. The students' responses will be flat and unnatural. Perhaps the greatest cause of this kind of student reaction is a poor role play scenario. Situations that are unrealistic or stifling will inevitably cause a negative reaction among your students. If you are teaching adolescents, they may simply refuse to participate.

- *Involve Students in Choices:* This is especially vital when working with teens, but is important with many adults as well. Offering choices may mean abandoning your scenarios in favor of ones that the students want to dramatize. You should not offer to skip the role play if at all possible - with time, and gentle modeling, I find that almost any group of learners can come to appreciate this type of teaching.

- *"I Pass":* The ability to choose not to participate is vital, and may be life-saving for your role play. Who among us does not remember trying to hide behind the student in front of us as children when a difficult problem was posed by the teacher? "Please don't let her call on me" should not have to be the prayer of a student in your class.

- *Project Confidence:* If you are fearful that no one will choose to participate in your role play, your students may sense your anxiety. With difficult, reticent groups, I've found a graphic role play done by me to be quite amazing as an icebreaker.

- *Brief the Class:* Inexperienced students will require more guidance than experienced ones, but all students should be given the briefest instruction possible. Latitude in character responses may permit true emotions to surface.

- *Casting the Players:* First and foremost, seek volunteers. Don't force. It's interesting to cast roles against personality type (for example, casting a quiet student in a boisterous role). Step back and watch! Also, consider asking people in adversary roles to switch places and play the role of the person they've been opposing. (Christensen, Garvin, and Sweet, 1991)

- *Stop the Role Play at a Positive Point:* End while things are going well, before the students' become bored. One segment of a role play typically lasts from 10 - 15 minutes.

- *Lead a Follow-up Discussion after the Role Play:* This should involve the entire class, and should be open and thought-provoking, and should analyze the approaches made by the characters.

- *Have Fun and Enjoy!* Joy is a contagious human emotion. If the educator feels comfortable and at ease, and is obviously having a good time, then his/her students are more than likely going to emulate that affect.

Evaluation

To teach is to learn

.... Japanese Proverb

Professional Evaluation

I can guess what you must be thinking: Don't we ever get to avoid an evaluation?

Sure, you do. This, like everything else I present, has an "I Pass"....but......I would be thrilled to hear from you. "Birthing" this manual came at a difficult time for me. During the time when I was putting finishing touches on *Games Educators Play*, I lost my dear papa to cancer. There were times when, just as in labor and birth, I wondered what I was doing here!

Now that the effort is completed, I'm most interested in your feedback. If I could, I would present this material (and other topics) to you directly. I think I've come to enjoy presenting workshops to professionals almost as much as I enjoy working with teens. Since I can't meet and know each of you, however, your feedback will have to be the next best thing. IF you want to complete this evaluation, simply tear it out or copy it

(I'd copy it, if I were you. Who knows - the manual may fall apart, for all I know!)

Fill it out and mail it to me at:

Mary Jo Podgurski
Academy for Adolescent Health, Inc.
440 Washington Trust Building
Washington, Pa 15301
Phone (724) 222-2311
FAX (724) 222-5406
Toll Free 1 (888) 301-2311

Or, check us out on the internet @ **www.healthyteens.com**
My e-mail address is podmj@healthyteens.com

Thanks for your feedback, and as always, thanks for being "out there."

With friendship,

Mary Jo

Professional Evaluation
Games Educators Play Manual

IN GENERAL: The Games Educators Play Manual: (Please check all that apply)

_____ Will be relevant to my work   _____ Will not be relevant to my work
_____ Satisfied my expectations   _____ Was a waste of money
          _____ Will improve my interactive teaching
      _____ Won't improve my skills, but convinced me that my teaching is OK as it is

EVALUATION: Please rate the manual using a scale of 1 (poor) to 5 (excellent)

	1	2	3	4	5
	☹		😐		☺
1. FORMAT: How effective was the manual's format	_____	_____	_____	_____	_____
2. ORGANIZATION: Was the material presented in an organized manner?	_____	_____	_____	_____	_____
3. CLARITY: Were the instructions clear?	_____	_____	_____	_____	_____
4. CONTENT: How helpful was the content?	_____	_____	_____	_____	_____
5. OVERALL RATING: How would you rate the manual overall	_____	_____	_____	_____	_____

NEEDS ASSESSMENT: Please rate any games you played:

A. The game(s) I played was(were):

_____
_____
_____

B. Did the game you tried "click" with your students? _____ Yes _____ No

C. Do you have any comments about the games:

_____
_____
_____

Thank you so much! ONE KID AT A TIME!

Notes

Bibliography

Man's power to change himself,
that is, to learn,
is perhaps the most
impressive thing
about him

.... Edward Thorndike

Bibliography - Interactive Games and Role Play

"Teaching is not like inducing a chemical reaction: it is much more like painting a picture or making a piece of music...."

from **The Art of Teaching** by Gilbert Highet

Christensen, C./R., Garvin, D.A., and Sweet, A. (eds) (1991) Education for Judgment: The Artistry of Discussion Leadership, Boston: Harvard Business School

Davis, B. G., Tools for Teaching, (1993) San Francisco: Jossey-Bass Publishers

Driscoll, M., (1994) Physiology of Learning for Instruction, Allyn & Bacon, Boston

Frederick, P. (1981) "The Dreaded Discussion: Ten Ways to Start," Improving College and University Teaching, 29 (3), 109-114.

Fuhrmann, B.S., and Grasha, A. F., (1983) A Practical Handbook for College Teachers, Boston: Little, Brown

Gredler, M., (1992) Learning and Instruction: Theory into Practice, Prentice Hall, Inc., Simon & Shuster, New York

Highet, G., (1989) The Art of Teaching, New York: Vintage Books

Mayer, R., (1992) Thinking, Problem Solving, Cognition, W.H. Freeman and Company, New York

Maynard-Smith, J., The Evolution and Theory of Games, Cambridge University Press, 1982

McKeache, W.J., (1991) Teaching Tips. (8th Ed.) Lexington, Massachusetts

Nichols, F., and Hummenick, S., (1988) Childbirth Education: Practice, Research, and Theory, Philadelphia, W.B. Saunders, Inc.

Podgurski, M.J., (1989) Postpone, Prevent, Prepare, publication pending, Academypress

Pryor, K., (1983) Don't Shoot the Dog: The New Art of Teaching and Training, New York: Bantam Books

Tannen, D., (1990) You Just Don't Understand: Women and Men in Conversation, New York: Ballentine Books,

Adolescent Bibliography

Alan Guttmacher Institute, (1994) Sex and America's Teenagers, New York and Washington

Blankenhorn, D.,(1995) Fatherless in America: Confronting our Most Urgent Social Problem, Basic Books, Harper Collins Publishers

Brinkley, G., & Sampson, (1989) S., Young and Pregnant - A Book for You, Pink, Inc., Atlantic Beach, FlaColes, R., & Stokes, G.,

Concordia Press, (1988) Learning About Sex Series: Volumes 1 through 6, St. Louis, Missouri

Coontz, S., (1992) The Way We Never Were: American Families and the Nostalgia Trap, Basic Books, Harper Collins Publisher, New York, 1992

Crewdson, J., (1988) By Silence Betrayed: Sexual Abuse of Children in America, New York, Harper & Row

Dash, L, (1989) When Children Want Children - An Inside Look at the Crisis of Teenage Parenthood, New York, Penguin Book

Doak, C., Doak, L, & Root, J., (1985) Teaching Patients with Low Literacy Skills, Philadelphia: Lippincott

Edelman, MW, (1995) Guide my Feet: Prayers and Meditations on Loving and Working with Chidlren, Beacon Press, Boston, MA

Godby-Johnson, A., (1993) A Rock and A Hard Place - One Boy's Triumphant Story. New York, Crown Publishers

Kittredge, M., (1992) Teens with AIDS Speak Out, New Jersey, Simon & Shuster,

Luker, K., (1996) Dubious Conceptions: The Politics of Teenage Pregnancy, Harvard University Press, Massachusetts

Pipher, M., (1995) Reviving Ophelia: Saving the Selves of Adolescent Girls, Ballantine Books, New York

Podgurski, M.J., (1993) School Based Adolescent Pregnancy Classes, AWHONN's Clinical Issues in Perinatal and Women's Health Nursing, Volume 4, Number 1, Lippincott

Robinson, B., (1988) Teenage Fathers, Lexington Books: D.C. Heath and Co.

Zabin, L., & Hirsch, M., (1988) Evaluation of Pregnancy Prevention Programs in the School Context, Lexington Books, Massachusetts

Possible Music for Name that Tune Game

The following are only examples of musical selections. Be creative and choose your own.

All One Tribe. Scott Fitzgerald, World Disc Productions, Inc. 915 Spring street, Friday Harbor, San Juan Island, Washington 98250

(The) Fairy Ring, Mike Rowland, Music Design, Inc., 207 E. Buffalo, Milwaukee, WI, 53202

George Winston, *Summer or Winter into Spring,* Windham Hill Records, Box 9388, Stanford, CA 94305

Humanity: On Wings of Song, Spring Hill Music, Box 800, Boulder, Colo 80306

Lorie Line: *Beyond A Dream; Walking with You; Out of Line* Produced by Time Line Productions, PO Box 251, Excelsior, MN 55331 *(Piano music of popular pieces, for example, The Secret Garden, Les Mes - A Little Fall of Rain, Prince of Tides, Wind Beneath my Wings)*

(The) Mystic Sea, Madacy Music, Inc. Box 1445 St. Laurent, Quebec, Canada H4L4Z1

Rain Dance, Philip Elcano, Desert Productions, Box 6913, Reno, Nevada 89513

Still on the Journey, Sweet Honey in the Rock, Warner Bros Records

Timeless Motion, Daniel Kobialka, Li-Sem Enterprises, Inc. 490 El Camino Road, Suite 215, Belmont, CA 94002

Transitions - (womb sounds) Placenta Music, Inc. 2675 Acorn Aven, NE, Atlanta, GA 30305

The World Sings Goodnight: Lullabies of 33 Cultures Sung in their Native Tongue, Sales benefit Amnesty International - call 1 -800 -Amnesty

Any of Kenny G's instrumentals

Any flute instrumental by R. Carlos Nakai

Any popular movie soundtrack with an instrumental component, for example, *Far and Away, The Last of the Mohicans*

Acknowledgments

The future has many names:
For the weak, it is the impossible
For the fainthearted, it is the unknown
For the thoughtful and valiant, it is the ideal
The Challenge is great
The Task is large
The Time is NOW

....Victor Hugo

Games Educators Play
ACKNOWLEDGMENTS

No effort exists alone.

Please allow me to thank some of the many people who inspire and support my work:

My Family: Rich, Amy, Lisa, and Nathan
Thank you for always being there.
My dear Lisa - Without your help, this project would not have come to fruition

My Parents
You gave me the greatest gift of all - a nurturing childhood.
Good or bad, childhood lasts a lifetime.

My Students
By listening to you I have truly been educated

My Dear Friend Helen Romano
Without your support and vision, the Outreach would never have happened

My Colleagues
You have to deal with working with the "Sex Lady!"
Thank you for loving kids and making this so much more than a job

The Teen Outreach Parents
You know who you are, and you know how much I thank you.
Few people know the truth of the effort you put into parenting.

My Dear Friend Tony and his Mom
You continue to inspire me and model courage, spirit, and humanity.

Finally, and most important, I acknowledge with
humility the strength I am given spiritually.
No matter how difficult the day may appear, I know I never face it alone.

ONE KID AT A TIME!™